Real Numbers

PRENTICE-HALL INTERNATIONAL, INC. *London*
PRENTICE-HALL OF AUSTRALIA, PTY., LTD. *Sydney*
PRENTICE-HALL OF CANADA, LTD. *Toronto*
PRENTICE-HALL OF INDIA (PRIVATE) LTD. *New Delhi*
PRENTICE-HALL OF JAPAN, INC. *Tokyo*
PRENTICE-HALL DE MEXICO, S.A. *Mexico City*

Stefan Drobot

PROFESSOR OF MATHEMATICS
THE OHIO STATE UNIVERSITY

PRENTICE-HALL, INC.   ENGLEWOOD CLIFFS, NEW JERSEY

Real Numbers

Real Numbers
by Stefan Drobot

Preface

The content of this book is based on lectures sponsored by the National Science Foundation and given to high-school teachers at the University of Notre Dame during the summer sessions 1961–63.

Stress has been put on underlying ideas and motivation, rather than on elaboration of all the details. Some parts, however, have been worked out more pedantically, as illustrations of mathematical formalism. Thus, the book is not a systematic or complete course on the subject indicated by its title. There are rather informal talks on real numbers, intended to give a better understanding of the concepts involved, their historical and logical development, and their location in some parts of mathematical thought.

The lectures have been inspired by Dr. Arnold E. Ross to whom I wish to express my gratitude.

STEFAN DROBOT

Contents

Real Numbers

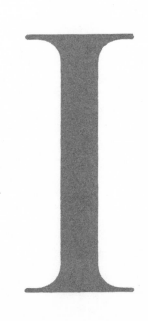

The Concept of Real Numbers

I. Historical and Logical Development

The study of numbers starts with *natural* numbers, $(1, 2, 3, \ldots)$, passes to *fractions* (e.g., $1/2$, $2/3$, $10/7$, ...), to *rational* numbers, including *integers* (e.g., 0, $-4/5$, $3/4$, -2, ...), and then to *real* numbers (e.g., $\sqrt{2}$, $\sqrt[3]{-5/4}$, π, ...). *Complex* numbers (e.g., $2/3 + 4\sqrt{-1}$) will not be discussed in detail in this book.

These successively generalized kinds of numbers were historically developed in approximately that order. Natural numbers have been used since time immemorial; fractions were employed by the ancient Egyptians as early as 1700 B.C.; and the Pythagoreans in ancient Greece, about 400 B.C., discovered numbers, like $\sqrt{2}$, which cannot be fractions. The argument ran as follows: Should $\sqrt{2}$ be a fraction n/d in its *lowest terms*, then $n^2 = 2d^2$ would imply that the (natural) numerator n is even; thus n^2 divisible by 4, whence the (natural) denominator d would also be even, contrary to the supposition that n/d is in its lowest terms.

This discovery clashed with the philosophical and religious views to such an extent that it was dangerous to divulge it to the profane. Over the door of the Platonian Academy was inscribed: "No admittance for those not proficient in geometry." Not long before, Socrates had been sentenced to death for other "novel practices."

During the Middle Ages, both rational and irrational numbers were employed without concern. The notion of zero and negative numbers, as opposed to positive ones, was developed in India about the sixth century A.D. The signs "$+$" and "$-$," however, date only from the fourteenth century.

About the same time, the "imaginary" numbers (e.g., $\sqrt{-1}$) started thrusting themselves into mathematics. The very terms "real" and "imaginary" indicate that these concepts were not adopted without apprehension. But even some rules for real numbers, like $(-1)(-1) = +1$, were considered mysterious.

The concept of a number was associated with the geometrical concept of a point, and these two terms are still used as synonyms. Geometry, connected closely with the human organ of sight and its scanning ability, was more appealing than logical deduction. In many ancient books the proofs, even of arithmetical facts, were given by a geometrical picture with no verbal explanation. Diagrams are still helpful both in learning and in teaching.

Thus, it seemed evident that the natural numbers correspond to a discrete sequence of points going in one direction of a straight line; the integers to their prolongation to the other direction; the rational numbers correspond to points obtained by dividing the intervals into smaller parts. The ancient Greeks knew, however, that this interpolation leaves out many points—in fact, all those corresponding to irrationals, like $\sqrt{2}$—and the number $\sqrt{2}$ itself was understood as the length of the diagonal of a unit square. The "evident" fact that the line is *continuous* motivated the acceptance of the "existence" of real numbers. But the meaning of *continuity* itself was not explained, despite many attempts to do so. This was in striking and challenging contrast to the rigorous spirit of geometry, constructed axiomatically as early as 300 B.C. in Euclid's "Elements." The notion of continuity of real numbers, as well as the very concept of numbers, was not separated from geometrical arguments until the nineteenth century, when it was based on more general foundations of the *theory of sets* and *formal logic.*

The deductive construction of various kinds of numbers imitates, to a certain extent, their historical development. It starts with an *axiomatic theory* of natural numbers. Its first pattern was given in 1891 by G. Peano. Having constructed arithmetic of naturals, one can continue without additional axioms to generalize the concept of number, using only set theory and formal logic. We shall give an outline of that approach.

In *Peano arithmetic,* natural numbers are considered elements of a set in which one assumes without definition one *primitive term*: the successor to a natural number. The following *axioms* are also assumed without proof: (1) Two natural numbers are equal if and only if their successors are equal; (2) in the set considered there exists an element, denoted by 1, which is not a successor; (3) the axiom of Mathematical Induction: If 1 belongs to a set T of natural numbers, and if the belonging to T of any natural number t implies the belonging to T of the successor of t, then every natural number belongs to T.

It can be proved that Mathematical Induction is logically equivalent with the following *Well Ordering axiom:* Every (not empty) subset of natural numbers contains an element that is not a successor to any element of that set.

There is still another proposition logically equivalent with Mathematical Induction, which is customarily formulated in a picturesque way:

Dirichlet Box Principle: If there are more apples than boxes, and we put all the apples into the boxes, then in at least one box there will be more than one apple.

Of course, this should be stated in the language of arithmetic of natural numbers, which does not use words like "apple" or "box." This can be done, and the equivalence with Mathematical Induction can be proved formally.

The arithmetic of natural numbers can be developed from the Peano axioms by *defining* new notions and *proving* theorems. The only tools used in this deduction are set theory and formal logic. Thus, for example, one defines addition, multiplication, the relation of "being smaller" ($<$), and one proves all the familiar rules. The chain of reasoning may be quite long but it can be carried out.[1]

The generalization of natural numbers to integers, then to rationals, and then to real numbers, requires no additional primitive terms or axioms.

Thus, integer numbers, among which subtraction is always possible, can be constructed by the following idea. Consider all the possible ordered pairs a_1-a_2 of natural numbers, and call two such pairs, a_1-a_2 and a_1'-a_2', *equivalent* if

$$a_1 + a_2 = a_1' + a_2'.$$

The hyphen "-" is, from a formal point of view, not the sign "minus"; it indicates coupling of two natural numbers, a_1 and a_2, into an ordered pair, considering the equivalence of such pairs with respect to the addition operation $+$, known already from the arithmetic of natural numbers.

Let A denote the set of all those pairs equivalent with each other, a_1-a_2, a_1'-a_2', etc.; let B denote another, different set of pairs, b_1-b_2, b_1'-b_2' etc., also equivalent with each other. We *define* $A, B, \ldots$ as the *integer* numbers. We must not be confused by the fact that integer numbers have been defined as sets. We have been using set theory and formal logic only.

After this construction we must develop anew the arithmetic of integers. This is done by an appropriate redefining of all the counterparts known for natural numbers (e.g., addition, $A + B$, multiplication, $A \times B$, ordering, $A < B$, etc.) and by defining new elements that do not have their counterparts among the naturals, (e.g., zero or negative numbers). This program can be carried out also.[2]

From integers we pass to the rational numbers in a way analogous to that by which the integers have been constructed from the naturals.

Consider all the possible ordered pairs A_1/A_2 of integers, for which the second element, A_2, is not zero, and call two such pairs, A_1/A_2, A_1'/A_2', equivalent if $A_1 \times A_2' = A_1' \times A_2$. Here, again, the slant "/" is, from a formal point of view, not the sign of division; it indicates the coupling of two integers, A_1 and A_2, into an ordered pair, considering the equivalence of such pairs with respect to the multiplication operation ($\times$), known already from the previously developed arithmetic of integers. Let $\mathscr{A}$ denote the set of all those pairs A_1/A_2, A_1'/A_2', etc. equivalent with each other ; let $\mathscr{B}$ denote another, different set of pairs B_1/B_2, B_1'/B_2', etc., also equivalent with each other. We *define* $\mathscr{A}$, $\mathscr{B}$, ... as the *rational* numbers. Again, we have to develop anew the arithmetic of rationals by redefining all the counterparts known already for integers and by defining new elements (e.g., fractions, which do not have their counterparts among the integers).

> We could have passed from naturals first to fractions by using equivalence with respect to multiplication, and then from fractions to rational numbers, by using equivalence with respect to addition. The historical development actually followed this pattern.

The passage from rationals to the real numbers differs essentially from the two previously described. Integers were defined by the use of *pairs* of naturals, and rational numbers were defined by the use of *pairs* of integers. However, we cannot pass from rationals to real numbers by using pairs of rationals, or even sets of any finite number of rationals. We must use sets of *infinitely many* rationals to get continuity among real numbers.

Various methods are known for introducing real numbers and the concept of continuity at the same time, using set-theoretical concepts only. All such methods have been proved to be logically equivalent.

One method, worked out in 1872 by R. Dedekind, is described here. Divide the set of all rational numbers into two distinct subsets, called the lower class α and the upper class α', in such a way that every rational of the lower class is smaller than any rational of the upper class. This is called a *Dedekind cut*. There are infinitely many such cuts. Given a fixed cut, one of its classes, say the lower one, is defined as the real number α. Thus, a real number is defined by an *infinite* set— namely, the lower class. This not only defines a real number, but also, at the same time, the very concept of *continuity*.

From this point of view, there is *no* continuity among the *rational* numbers. In fact, there may be no *rational* number that is both the greatest in the lower class and the smallest in the upper class. For example, if the lower class consists of all rationals the square of which is less than 2 (and of all negatives) and the upper class consists of all other rationals, there is no *rational* number making the cut. However, by defining a real number as the cut itself we automatically fill up all the "gaps," and also define the continuity itself.

From the formal point of view, we have to develop anew the arithmetic of real numbers defined as Dedekind cuts. This is possible, however cumbersome it may be.[3]

Another way of defining real numbers and continuity among them was introduced about the same time by G. Cantor. It uses the concept of an *infinite sequence* of rational numbers and the property that such a sequence is *convergent* without specifying to what. Both notions can be defined by using *rational* numbers only. It may happen that some convergent sequences of rational numbers converge *to a rational* number, but others do not, even though they are *convergent*. For instance, the sequence of rationals:

$$1, \left(1 + \frac{1}{1}\right), \left(1 + \frac{1}{1} + \frac{1}{1 \cdot 2}\right), \left(1 + \frac{1}{1} + \frac{1}{1 \cdot 2} + \frac{1}{1 \cdot 2 \cdot 3}\right), \ldots$$

is convergent, but not *to a rational* number. See page 28.

Call two convergent sequences of rationals equivalent if the sequence of the differences of the corresponding terms is convergent to 0. Consider all the possible sets of equivalent convergent sequences. These are by Cantor's definition real numbers, which, again, involves infinite sets.

It can be proved that the arithmetic of real numbers defined by Dedekind cuts, as well as that based on Cantor's definition, are completely analogous— in fact, exactly the same. Moreover, it is possible to state and to prove a theorem which expresses more explicitly the fact that there is continuity among real numbers. This can be done as follows.

Call a set of real numbers *bounded from above* if all its members are not greater than some real number, called the *upper bound* for that set.

There are infinitely many upper bounds for any given set bounded from above. The continuity among real numbers is now expressed by the following condition: For any set of real numbers bounded from above there exists always a real number which is the *least upper bound* for that set.

Notice that the least upper bound for a set need not belong to that set. Furthermore, from that condition, it follows that for any set of real numbers bounded from *below* there exists a *greatest lower bound*. To prove this take a set consisting of elements negative to the elements of the original set. Thus, continuity can be expressed also by using the greatest lower bound; i.e., the existence of either one of those bounds can be assumed as a condition defining the concept of real numbers.

It can also be proved that this condition is logically equivalent to the following two:

(1) **Archimedean axiom:** For any real number γ there exists a natural number n greater than γ.

(2) **Cantor-Ascoli axiom:** Every infinite sequence of closed intervals, each of which is nested in the previous one, contains a number belonging to all of these intervals.

Here is one more equivalent condition.

(3) **Bolzano axiom:** For every infinite set of real numbers, bounded from both sides, there exists at least one *point of accumulation*—i.e., a real number such that every interval containing it must contain at least one different element of the set considered. (The point of accumulation need not belong to that set).

There exist other logically equivalent methods of passing from rationals to real numbers that use only set-theory and formal logic. All such methods involve sets of *infinitely many* rationals.

Somehow, between the rational and the real numbers, the *algebraic* numbers are constructed by use of only finite sets of rationals. A number x is called algebraic, of degree n, if it satisfies some equation of the form

$$a_0 x^n + a_1 x^{n-1} + \ldots + a_{n-1} x + a_n = 0$$

with *rational* coefficients, $a_0, \ldots, a_n$, and does not satisfy any other such equation with order less than n. Among algebraic numbers are all the rationals which are algebraic of degree 1. However, there are also many irrational numbers (e.g., $\sqrt{2}, \sqrt[3]{5} + \sqrt{3/7}$, etc.), and the distinction between rational and irrational numbers can somehow be smoothed, the set of all algebraic numbers being larger than the set of all rationals. It is not large enough, however, to embrace all real numbers. In fact, in 1851, J. Liouville proved that there are real numbers, called *transcendental*, which cannot be algebraic (see page 68). Consequently, there is still no continuity among algebraic numbers.

Among algebraic numbers, however, there are also some complex numbers. For instance, $\sqrt{-1}$ is an algebraic number, because it satisfies the equation $x^2 + 1 = 0$. But not every complex number is algebraic. On the other hand, *all* complex numbers can be obtained from the reals by using only pairs, thus *finite* sets, of real numbers. In fact, every complex number is of the form $\alpha + \beta \sqrt{-1}$, with real α and β. There is continuity among complex numbers. This is "evident" from a geometrical point of view if the complex numbers are interpreted as points on the plane.

We shall conclude with some methodological comments. The substratum from which the concept of numbers was developed consists of theory of sets and formal logic, which are considered now as basic and common to all mathematical theories. Though formal logic can be traced back through history to antiquity, the theory of sets was created about 1870 by G. Cantor.[4] We will assume an understanding of the language of these basic theories: in set theory the terms "set" (synonyms: class, collection), "elements," "belong," "subset," "relation" (between elements), "operation" (on elements), "function"; in formal logic the terms "if," "and," "or," "now," "every," "some," "equal," "true."

The word "some" as used in mathematics is synonymous with "there exists." "Existence" is not to be understood here in a philosophical sense (if there exists any), but refers always to a definite set under consideration. Also, the word "equal" is a *logical* term, assumed to be (1) *reflective*; i.e., $x = x$, whatever x means; (2) *symmetric*; i.e., if $x = y$, then $y = x$; (3) *transitive*; i.e., if $x = y$ and $y = z$, then $x = z$; and (4) *substitutive*;

i.e., if $x = y$, then every proposition true for x is also true for y. Notice that there is no "if" in reflexivity.

An axiomatic theory assumes certain *primitive terms* without definition and certain statements, called *axioms*, without proof. Then, by use of set theory and formal logic, further concepts are defined and further statements, called theorems, are proved.

In the deductive development of the concept of real numbers, outlined previously, the only axiomatic theory was Peano arithmetic of natural numbers. The arithmetics of integers, rationals, and real numbers were superstructions built up by means of set theory and formal logic alone. However, at each stage, we could have assumed the respective arithmetic axiomatically without reference to the previous ones. Thus, for example, we can assume axiomatically the arithmetic of integers, independent of Peano arithmetic but including the concept of natural numbers,[5] or the arithmetic of rationals, independent of their deductive construction from naturals and then integers. A direct axiomatization of the arithmetic of real numbers is outlined in Section 2.

2. Axiomatic of Real Numbers

Real numbers, $\alpha, \beta, \gamma, \ldots$, are elements of a set satisfying the following axioms, which are divided for further comments into groups marked by the letters N, I, Q, R.

N. There are, in the set, two operations: Addition, $\alpha + \beta$, and multiplication, $\alpha\beta$, which, when performed on any pair of elements, produce an element of the same set. Addition is *commutative*; i.e.,

$$\alpha + \beta = \beta + \alpha$$

and *associative*; i.e.,

$$(\alpha + \beta) + \gamma = \alpha + (\beta + \gamma)$$

Multiplication is also commutative and associative; i.e.,

$$\alpha\beta = \beta\alpha \quad \text{and} \quad (\alpha\beta)\gamma = \alpha(\beta\gamma)$$

Multiplication is also *distributive* with respect to addition; i.e.,

$$(\alpha + \beta)\gamma = \alpha\gamma + \beta\gamma$$

There exists, in the set, a unit element, 1, such that $1\alpha = \alpha$ for every α.

There is, in the set, an *ordering* relation, $\alpha < \beta$, between any pair of elements. This relation is *trichotomic*; i.e., for any α and β, one and only one of the cases holds:

$$\alpha < \beta, \quad \alpha = \beta, \quad \beta < \alpha$$

It is also *transitive*; i.e., if

$$\alpha < \beta \quad \text{and} \quad \beta < \gamma, \quad \text{then} \quad \alpha < \gamma$$

Addition is *monotonic*; i.e., if

$$\alpha < \beta, \quad \text{then} \quad \alpha + \gamma < \beta + \gamma$$

for every γ.

I. There exists an element zero, 0, such that

$$\alpha + 0 = \alpha$$

for every α. Besides, $0 < 1$. There exists for every α its negative, $-\alpha$, such that

$$\alpha + (-\alpha) = 0$$

Multiplication is *monotonic*; i.e., if

$$\alpha < \beta \quad \text{and} \quad 0 < \gamma, \quad \text{then} \quad \alpha\gamma < \beta\gamma$$

Q. There exists for every α except 0, its inverse, $\dfrac{1}{\alpha}$, such that

$$\alpha \frac{1}{\alpha} = 1$$

R. Continuity of Real Numbers. For every set of real numbers bounded from above there exists a real number which is the *least upper bound* for that set.

In order to illustrate how the arithmetic of real numbers can be derived from these axioms, we shall prove some theorems and define some concepts.

1. The element 1 is *unique*. Should there be another, $1'$, then commutativity of multiplication would imply

$$1' = 1 \cdot 1' = 1' \cdot 1 = 1$$

contrary to the supposition that $1' \neq 1$.

2. Cancellation law for addition: If

$$\alpha + \gamma = \beta + \gamma \quad \text{then} \quad \alpha = \beta$$

Should $\alpha \neq \beta$, then by trichotomy it would be either

$$\alpha < \beta \quad \text{or} \quad \beta < \alpha,$$

which, by monotony of addition and trichotomy, again, would imply that either

$$\alpha + \gamma < \beta + \gamma \quad \text{or} \quad \beta + \gamma < \alpha + \gamma$$

contrary to the supposition that

$$\alpha + \gamma = \beta + \gamma$$

Notice that we have used here the axioms of the group N only.

3. To prove that $0\alpha = 0$, write

$$\beta\alpha + 0\alpha = (\beta + 0)\alpha = \beta\alpha = \beta\alpha + 0$$

Here we have used distributivity, the existence of 0, and the cancellation law proved in 2 above.

4. To prove that $(-1)\alpha = -\alpha$ write

$$\alpha + (-\alpha) = 0 = 0\alpha = (1 + (-1))\alpha = 1\alpha + (-1)\alpha = \alpha + (-1)\alpha$$

and use the cancellation law; here we have used the existence of negative, the equality $0\alpha = 0$ proved in 3, distributivity, and existence of 1.

5. To prove that $\alpha < \beta$ implies $-\beta < -\alpha$, write

$$\alpha + (-\alpha) + (-\beta) < \beta + (-\alpha) + (-\beta)$$

by using commutativity and monotony of addition. It follows also that if $\alpha > 0$, then $-\alpha < 0$.

6. To prove that $(-1)(-1) = 1$, write

$$1 + (-1) = 0 = (-1)0 = (-1)(-1 + 1)$$
$$= (-1)(-1) + (-1)1$$
$$= (-1)(-1) + (-1)$$

and cancel (-1) in the first and last terms. Which axioms and theorems have been employed?

7. Cancellation law for multiplication: If

$$\alpha\gamma = \beta\gamma \quad \text{and} \quad \gamma \neq 0, \quad \text{then} \quad \alpha = \beta$$

Write

$$\beta = 1\beta = \left(\frac{1}{\gamma}\gamma\right)\beta = \frac{1}{\gamma}(\gamma\beta) = \frac{1}{\gamma}(\gamma\alpha) = 1\alpha = \alpha$$

Here the following axioms have been used: existence of inverse $\dfrac{1}{\gamma}$, associativity and commutativity of multiplication, and the existence of 1.

8. Proof that there are *no divisors of zero*: If

$$\alpha\beta = 0, \quad \text{then} \quad \alpha = 0 \quad \text{or} \quad \beta = 0.$$

Should $\alpha \neq 0$ *and* $\beta \neq 0$, then by cancelling the equality $\beta\alpha = 0\alpha$ by α we would get $\beta = 0$, contrary to the supposition that $\beta \neq 0$.

9. The absolute value $|\alpha|$ of a real number α is defined as follows: If $\alpha \geq 0$, then $|\alpha| = \alpha$; if $\alpha < 0$ then $|\alpha| = -\alpha$. All the familiar rules for the absolute value can be proved by definition, axioms, and previously proved theorems. For example, $|\alpha| = |-\alpha|$; if $\alpha \neq 0$ then $|\alpha| > 0$; there is $|\alpha| < \beta$ if and only if $-\beta < \alpha < \beta$. We leave detailed proofs to the reader. Here are two other properties of the absolute value.

10. The triangle inequality:

$$\big|\,|\alpha| - |\beta|\,\big| \leq |\alpha \pm \beta| \leq |\alpha| + |\beta|$$

We get the right-hand side inequality by adding

$$-|\alpha| \leq \alpha \leq |\alpha| \quad \text{and} \quad -|\beta| \leq |\beta| \leq \beta$$

The left-hand side follows from

$$|(\alpha \pm \beta) \mp \beta| \leq |\alpha \pm \beta| + |\beta|$$

and

$$|(\beta \pm \alpha) \mp \alpha| \leq |\alpha \pm \beta| + |\alpha|$$

and previously proved rules.

11. Interval (α, γ) is the set of real numbers β for which $\alpha < \beta < \gamma$. If α or γ or both α and γ are included, the set is called a closed interval $[\alpha, \gamma)$, $(\alpha, \gamma]$, (on left or right, respectively) or $[\alpha, \gamma]$.

It is sometimes convenient to consider an interval without specifying which end, α or γ, is left or right.

A real number β is *between* α and γ, i.e.,

$$\alpha \leq \beta \leq \gamma \quad \text{or} \quad \gamma \leq \beta \leq \alpha$$

if and only if

$$|\alpha - \beta| + |\beta - \gamma| = |\alpha - \gamma|.$$

For example, if $\alpha \leq \beta \leq \gamma$, then

$$|\alpha - \gamma| = \gamma - \alpha = \gamma - \beta + \beta - \alpha = |\gamma - \beta| + |\beta - \alpha|$$

The same equality is true for $\gamma \leq \beta \leq \alpha$.

Conversely—provided the equality of absolute values

$$|\alpha - \beta| + |\beta - \gamma| = |\alpha - \gamma|$$

holds—if $\alpha \leq \gamma$, the supposition that $\beta < \alpha$ would give

$$|\alpha - \beta| + |\gamma - \alpha| = |\gamma - \beta|$$

which in turn gives by addition $|\alpha - \beta| = 0$; whence $\alpha = \beta$, contrary to the supposition that $\beta < \alpha$. The supposition $\gamma < \beta$ leads similarly to contradiction; and the theorem is proved analogously if $\gamma \leq \alpha$. This allows us to handle various separate cases simultaneously.

12. Characteristic property of the least upper bound. Let $\underline{\alpha}$ be the least upper bound of a set $\mathscr{A}$ of real numbers bounded from above. Then, for any real number $\beta < \underline{\alpha}$, there exists in $\mathscr{A}$ an element α_1, such that

$$\beta < \alpha_1 \leq \underline{\alpha}$$

This is actually a more precise formulation that α is the *least* of the upper bounds for the set $\mathscr{A}$. Hence, it follows that the least upper bound is *unique*. Notice that the least upper bound for a set need not belong to that set.

Analogously, if $\bar{\alpha}$ is the *greatest lower bound* for a set $\mathscr{B}$ bounded from below, then for $\gamma > \bar{\alpha}$, there exists in $\mathscr{B}$ an element α_2, such that

$$\gamma > \alpha_2 \geq \bar{\alpha}.$$

13. Natural numbers. From the formal point of view we must now define which of the real numbers, as defined by the assumed axioms, are to be considered naturals. The idea is to distinguish among the real numbers a subset of elements which satisfy the Peano axioms (see page 5).

The first axiom, viz. that two elements are equal if and only if their successors are equal, is readily satisfied by *all real* numbers, if we call $\alpha + 1$ the successor of α. However, the other Peano axioms are *not* satisfied in the *whole* set of *real* numbers. For example, the axiom requiring that 1 is not a successor is false, because in the whole set of real numbers 1 is a successor to 0. Also, the other Peano axiom, viz. Mathematical Induction, is not satisfied because the proposition "every element is >0" is false in the whole set of real numbers, while both premises of Mathematical Induction hold. Therefore, we shall *define* the class of natural numbers as the *subset* of *real* numbers for which 1 is not a successor, and for which Mathematical Induction holds.

These natural numbers as defined above, however, do not satisfy the axioms I and Q, but form a "smallest" subset of real numbers, satisfying the axiom N exclusively. In fact, those axioms can be proved as theorems in Peano arithmetic.

14. Integers, rationals. The *integer* numbers can now be defined as the "smallest" subset of natural numbers, satisfying only the axioms N and I. Again, the *rationals* are defined as the "smallest" set of real numbers satisfying only axioms N, I, and Q.

This arrangement of the axioms of real numbers imitates the historical development. It does not require formal change of the previously accepted axioms for the passage from naturals, then to integers, then to rationals, and finally to real numbers—each successive group I, Q, R, of the axioms requires only the *existence* of some new element, not stipulated by any of the previous groups. It also imitates the informal way we teach in schools.

In the assumed arrangement of axiomatic of real numbers the axioms stipulating the *ordering* (group N) and the axiom of continuity play essential parts. If we omit them and assume only the remaining axioms we will get an axiomatic description of an *algebraic field*, in which the two operations (addition and multiplication) and their inverses are essential. Systems described by an even smaller part of those algebraic axioms, or other modifications, are also considered in Abstract Algebra. However, no continuity is assumed in a "purely" algebraic theory. The main purpose in algebra for passing from natural numbers to integers was to make subtraction always possible; i.e., to make the difference between any two integers also an integer. Similarly, the purpose of introducing rationals was to make division (except by 0) always possible. Neither ordering relation nor continuity is needed in those successive generalizations. The passage to real numbers was motivated primarily by introducing continuity.

REFERENCES

(1) See C. C. MacDuffee, *An Introduction to Abstract Algebra.* (New York: John Wiley & Sons, Inc., 1940) pp. 1–8.

(2) See G. Birkhoff and S. MacLane, *A Survey of Modern Algebra*, 9th ed. (New York: The Macmillan Company, 1960) pp. 51–57.

(3) O. Perron, *Irrationalzahlen.* (Berlin: W. de Grúyter, 1960) Ch. I.

(4) Set theory and formal logic are discussed in R. L. Wilder, *Introduction to the Foundations of Mathematics.* (New York: John Wiley & Sons, Inc., 1956) where an extensive bibliography may be found. See also R. R. Stoll, *Sets, Logic and Axiomatic Theories.* (San Francisco: W. H. Freeman and Co., 1961).

(5) See Birkhoff and MacLane, *op. cit.* (2).

II

Digital Representations of Real Numbers

In this chapter various methods of representing real numbers by finite or infinite sequences of naturals are discussed.

I. Decimal and Cantor Expansions

The common *decimal expansion* of a real number consists in the following: Starting with the elements 0 and 1, given by the axiomatic of real numbers, denote $1 + 1 = 2, 2 + 1 = 3$, etc., up to 9, and $9 + 1 = 10$. By using the digits $0, \ldots, 9$ and a point, form the sequence

$$(1) \qquad c_m c_{m-1} \ldots c_1 c_0 . d_1 d_2 \ldots d_n \ldots$$

in which there is a finite number $(m + 1)$ of digits $c_m, \ldots, c_0$ before and a finite or infinite sequence of digits $d_1, d_2, \ldots$ after the point.

We could also assume that there are always infinitely many digits after the point by completing a finite sequence with 0's.

Let all the digits in (1) be given. They *represent* a real number in the following way. Consider the number

$$c = c_m 10^m + \ldots c_1 10 + c_0$$

and call it the *integer part*. Consider the set of rationals

(2) $$s_1 = \frac{d_1}{10}, \quad s_2 = \frac{d_1}{10} + \frac{d_2}{10^2}, \quad \ldots, \quad s_n = s_{n-1} + \frac{d_n}{10^n}$$

denoted later as $(d_1/10) + (d_2/10^2) + \ldots$. This set is bounded from above, because $0 \le d_n \le 9$. Thus

$$0 \le s_n \le \frac{9}{10} + \frac{9}{10^2} + \ldots + \frac{9}{10^n} = 1 - \frac{1}{10^n} < 1.$$

By the axiom of *continuity* there exists a unique real number α which is the least upper bound of the s_n's. We call α the *decimal part*.

In this way every decimal sequence (1) represents a unique real number $(c + \alpha)$.

By this definition, $c + \alpha$ is nonnegative. Sequences representing negative numbers are denoted by $-(c_m \ldots c_0.d_1 d_2 \ldots)$. In some uses, e.g., in mathematical tables, the decimal part is taken always as nonnegative, although the integer may be negative—for instance, $\bar{1}.8129$ stands for $-1 + .8129$.

If the decimal part is finite, then $\alpha = s_n$.

It follows by (2) that the partial sums s_n are increasing or not decreasing with the index n; i.e., $s_n \le s_{n+1}$. A geometrical interpretation is shown in Figure 1.

Figure 1

However, it is not true that every real number can be represented by a unique decimal sequence (1). For example, both $.999\ldots$ and $1.000\ldots$ represent the same number 1, because the least upper bound of $\frac{9}{10} + (\frac{9}{10})^2 + \ldots$ is 1. In fact, the nth member s_n of that set is less than 1; thus

1 is an *upper* bound. It is also the *least* upper bound, since a least
upper bound $\alpha < 1$ would imply

$$0 < 1 - \alpha \leq \frac{1}{10^n}$$

and since $10^n > n$ (proof by induction) it would be

$$n < \frac{1}{1 - \alpha}$$

for every natural n. However, this contradicts the Archimedean axiom
requiring that there exists a natural number n greater than $1/(1 - \alpha)$,
see page 9.

Therefore, we shall *exclude* decimal sequences (1) which end with a
series of consecutive 9's (right of the point). Then every real number can
be represented by a unique decimal sequence (1), called the *decimal
expansion* of the corresponding real number.

We shall summarize the argument above by stating and proving a
theorem. To this end, we introduce the following symbol: $[\xi]$ denotes
the greatest integer not exceeding ξ; i.e.,

(3) $$[\xi] \leq \xi < [\xi] + 1$$

For example: $$[\sqrt{3}] = 1, \quad [-40/7] = -6.$$

Theorem on Decimal Expansion. *Every real number* $0 \leq \alpha < 1$ *has
one and only one decimal expansion in which the digits are determined by
the following algorithm:*

Put $\rho_1 = \alpha$, *then* $d_1 = [10\rho_1]$. *If for some index n there is*

$$d_n = 10\rho_n$$

stop. If $d_n < 10\rho_n$ *put*

$$\rho_{n+1} = 10\rho_n - d_n$$

then

$$d_{n+1} = [10\rho_{n+1}].$$

The algorithm implies

(4) $$\rho_n = 10^{n-1}\alpha - [10^{n-1}\alpha]$$

(5) $$d_n = [10_n\alpha] - 10[10^{n-1}\alpha]$$

The partial sums s_n satisfy the inequalities

(6) $$0 \leq \alpha - s_{n+1} \leq \alpha - s_n < \frac{1}{10^n}$$

Before proving the theorem let us comment on it.

The partial sums, given by (2), *approximate* the real number α. They are rationals, $s_n = r_n/t_n$, with r_n integer and $t_n = 10^n$. Formula (6) shows that taking s_n instead of α guarantees a nonnegative *error* less than $1/10^n$. This holds, also, if the integer part c is included. For example, if we know that the decimal expansion of the number π starts with 3.14159, then taking this instead of π guarantees a nonnegative error less than $1/10^5$ which is less than .0004 per cent of the approximated π.

Formula (6) shows that the error of the approximation decreases or remains unchanged. The latter is the case when the nth digit is followed by 0. However, formula (5) assures that, in spite of all these "jerks" the error ultimately gets smaller and smaller. Compare page 39.

Let us illustrate now the algorithm for determining the digits by three examples.

Example 1. Let $\alpha = 3/40$. Put $\rho_1 = 3/40$; then

$$d_1 = [10\rho_1] = [30/40] = 0 < 10\rho_1$$

Put $\rho_2 = 10\rho_1 - d_1 = 3/4$; then

$$d_2 = [30/4] = 7 < 10\rho_2$$

Put $\rho_3 = 10\rho_2 - d_2 = 1/2$, then

$$d_3 = [10/2] = 5 = 10\rho_3$$

Stop. Thus, the decimal expansion of 3/40 is .075.

Example 2. Let $c + \alpha = 779/207 = 3 + 158/207$. Put $\rho_1 = 158/207$; then

$$d_1 = [1580/207] = 7 < 10\rho_1$$

Put $\rho_2 = 10\rho_1 - d_1 = 1580/207 - 7 = 131/207$; then

$$d_2 = [1310/207] = 6 < 10\rho_3$$

Continue this procedure to obtain for 779/207 an infinite and periodic decimal expansion

$$3.\lfloor 763285024154558933719806\rfloor 76\ldots$$

When approximating the number 779/207 by 3.7, the error, by formula (6), is less than 1/10, which is less than 5 per cent of the number approximated. Compare page 38.

Example 3. Let $c + \alpha = \sqrt{2} = 10\sqrt{2}/10$. Put $\rho_1 = \sqrt{2}/10$; then

$$d_1 = [\sqrt{2}] = 1 < 10\rho_1$$

because $1^2 < (\sqrt{2})^2 < 2^2$. Put $\rho_2 = 10\rho_1 - d_1 = \sqrt{2} - 1$, then

$$d_2 = [10\sqrt{2} - 10] = [10\sqrt{2}] - 10$$

In order to find $[10\sqrt{2}]$ we *try:*

$$10^2 = 100 < (10\sqrt{2})^2 = 200$$
$$11^2 = 121 < 200$$
$$12^2 = 144 < 200$$
$$13^2 = 169 < 200$$
$$14^2 = 196 < 200$$
$$15^2 = 225 > 200$$

Thus, $[10\sqrt{2}] = 14$, and $d_2 = 14 - 10 = 4$. Now, put

$$\rho_3 = (10\sqrt{2} - 10) - 4 = 10\sqrt{2} - 14$$

then

$$d_3 = [100\sqrt{2} - 140] = [100\sqrt{2}] - 140$$

In order to find $[100\sqrt{2}]$ *try* the formula again. It gives $[100\sqrt{2}] = 141$, and thus $d_3 = 141 - 140 = 1$. The first three digits of $\sqrt{2}$ are thus 1.41. The error, by formula (6), is less than 1/100, or about .7 per cent of $\sqrt{2}$. Compare page 39. Further digits of $\sqrt{2}$ must also be determined by trial and error. The digits *can* be uniquely determined, though a great deal of mechanical work is required to do so.

These examples show also that the ρ_n's in the decimal expansion

$$.d_1 d_2 \ldots d_{n-1} d_n d_{n+1} \ldots$$

are the remainders after replacing the first $(n - 1)$ digits by 0's; i.e.,

$$\rho_n = .00 \ldots 0 d_n d_{n+1} \ldots$$

Proof. That the number represented by digits $d_1 d_2 \ldots$ is *unique* follows from the uniqueness of the least upper bound. The part of the Theorem stating that, given α, the expansion $.d_1 d_2 \ldots$ is unique follows from formula (5) which determines all the digits uniquely. It will be proved presently.

Formula (4) follows by induction from the algorithm. In fact, for $n = 1$ there is

$$\rho_1 = 10^0\alpha - [10^0\alpha] = \alpha - [\alpha] = \alpha,$$

since $0 \leq \alpha < 1$. Assuming (4) true for some n, we have

$$\rho_{n+1} = 10\rho_n - [10\rho_n] = 10(10^{n-1}\alpha - [10^{n-1}\alpha]) - [10^n\alpha - 10[10^{n-1}\alpha]]$$
$$= 10^n\alpha - 10[10^{n-1}\alpha] - [10^n\alpha] + 10[10^{n-1}\alpha] = 10^n\alpha - [10^n\alpha],$$

thus, true for $(n + 1)$.

Formula (5) follows from (4). We have by the algorithm,

$$d_n = 10\rho_n - \rho_{n+1}$$

We substitute ρ_n and ρ_{n+1} given by (4) to get (5).

The inequality $0 \leq \alpha - s_n$ in (6) follows, since α is an *upper* bound of the s_n's. The inequality $\alpha - s_n < 1/10^n$ in (6) follows, because α is the *least* upper bound, and from the convention concerning 9's that implies that the number α represented by $.d_1d_2 \ldots d_nd_{n+1} \ldots$ is less than $.d_1d_2 \ldots d_n99 \ldots$, which is equal to $s_n + 1/10^n$, since $1/10^n$ is the least upper bound of $(9/10^n) + (9/10^{n+1}) + \ldots$.

Finally, the inequality $\alpha - s_{n+1} < \alpha - s_n$ follows directly from the definition (2) of the s_n's and from $d_n \geq 0$. This completes the entire proof.

Test for Rationality. *A number is rational if and only if its decimal expansion is either finite or periodic.*

Proof. If the decimal expansion is finite, then it represents a rational number by definition. If it is periodic: i.e., if

$$.d_1 \ldots d_k\overline{d_1} \ldots \overline{d_p}\overline{d_1} \ldots \overline{d_p} \ldots$$

denote $.0 \ldots 0\overline{d_1} \ldots \overline{d_p}$ by q, whence

$$\alpha = .d_1 \ldots d_k + q(.0 \ldots 10 \ldots 0 \ldots)$$

in which there are k zeros before the first digit 1 and $p-1$ zeros between the 1's. The last decimal represents the rational number $(10^{p-1})/10^p$; thus, α is rational.

Conversely, if α is rational, in its lowest terms, a/b, and $b \geq 1$, then we have by formula (4)

$$b\rho_n = 10^n a - b[10^{n-1}a/b]$$

which shows that $b\rho_n$ is an integer and nonnegative, since

$$0 \leq \rho_n < 1.$$

If $\rho_n = 0$ for some n, then the algorithm stops, and the decimal expansion is *finite*.

If for every n there is $0 < \rho_n < 1$, whence $0 < \rho_n b < b$, then the integer $\rho_n b$ can be one of the $(b - 1)$ naturals only: $1, 2, \ldots, (b - 1)$. According to the "box principle" (see page 5) at least two of the b integers $(b\rho_1, b\rho_2, \ldots, b\rho_b)$ must be equal—say

$$b\rho_k = b\rho_{k+p}$$

Thus, $\rho_k = \rho_{k+p}$. The algorithm for digits then implies by induction

$$\rho_{k+1} = \rho_{k+p+1}$$

and so on:

$$\rho_{k+r} = \rho_{k+p+r}$$

for any index r. By the algorithm the same follows for the digits; thus the expansion is *periodic*. This completes the proof.

Notice that in a decimal expansion an *infinite* sequence of digits can represent a *rational* number (e.g., $.33 \ldots = 1/3$). In this respect, the decimal expansion does not reflect the fact that a rational number can be defined by a pair, and thus by a *finite* set, of integers. It is so not only because of the arbitrary choice of the scale 10, but also because of the specific definition of the rationals s_n that approximate the number. Compare page 42.

The test implies that every (infinite) nonperiodic decimal expansion represents an irrational number. If we take the digits $0, 1, \ldots, 9$ at random, the chance of getting a periodic decimal is very small; most would be irrationals.

All the theorems proved on decimal expansion remain true if we use the base $b \geq 2$ rather than 10. The corresponding digits could be $0, 1, 2, \ldots (b - 1)$. Later, the term "decimal expansion" will be applied to both the decimal or to any other scale.

The word "digit" is synonymous with "finger." The smallest possible scale is 2, having two digits (0, 1) that occur explicitly in the axiomatic of real numbers (see page 12). The scale 2 is very convenient in theoretical investigations. It is also applied in electronic computers in which 1 corresponds to an electric impulse and 0 to lack of it.

The decimal expansion has been generalized by G. Cantor in the following way. Let

$$b_1, b_2, \ldots, b_n, \ldots$$

be a *fixed* infinite sequence of naturals greater than 1; i.e., $b_m \geq 2$ for all indices m. Form by the use of a point a finite or infinite sequence

(7) $$c_0 \cdot c_1 c_2 \ldots$$

which has the integer c_0 before the point, and the integers c_n after the point, such that

$$0 \leq c_n \leq b_n - 1$$

for any index n. Consider the set of rationals

(8) $$s_1 = \frac{c_1}{b_1}, \quad s_2 = \frac{c_1}{b_1} + \frac{c_2}{b_1 b_2}, \quad \ldots, s_n = s_{n-1} + \frac{c_n}{b_1 b_2 \ldots b_n}, \quad \ldots$$

In the English system of measure
$$\begin{aligned}
1 \text{ mile} &= 8 \text{ furlongs} = 8 \cdot 10 \text{ chains} = 8 \cdot 10 \cdot 22 \text{ yards} \\
&= 8 \cdot 10 \cdot 22 \cdot 3 \text{ feet} = 8 \cdot 10 \cdot 22 \cdot 3 \cdot 4 \text{ hands} \\
&= 8 \cdot 10 \cdot 22 \cdot 3 \cdot 4 \cdot 3 \text{ inches} \\
&= 8 \cdot 10 \cdot 22 \cdot 3 \cdot 4 \cdot 3 \cdot 12 \text{ lines}
\end{aligned}$$

Here, $b_1 = 8$, $b_2 = 10$, $b_3 = 22$, $b_4 = 3$, $b_5 = 4$, $b_6 = 3$, $b_7 = 12$. This could be continued ad infinitum to get an infinite sequence $b_1, b_2, \ldots$ (and to make that system of measure infinitely more awkward). Thus, a length of 9 miles 5 furlongs 7 chains 15 yards 2 feet 2 hands 2 inches 8 lines is a Cantor expansion: 0.957(15)2228.

The set (8) of partial sums is bounded from above by 1, because

$$\begin{aligned}
0 \leq s_n &\leq \frac{b_1 - 1}{b_1} + \frac{b_2 - 1}{b_1 b_2} + \ldots + \frac{b_n - 1}{b_1 b_2 \ldots b_n} \\
&= 1 - \frac{1}{b_1} + \frac{1}{b_1} - \frac{1}{b_1 b_2} + \frac{1}{b_1 b_2} - \ldots - \frac{1}{b_1 b_2 \ldots b_n} \\
&= 1 - \frac{1}{b_1 b_2 \ldots b_n} < 1
\end{aligned}$$

By the continuity axiom there exists a unique real number α that is the least upper bound for all the partial sums (8). The sequence $c_0 \cdot c_1 c_2 \ldots$ is called the *Cantor expansion* of the (nonnegative) number $c_0 + \alpha$.

By an argument similar to that used for decimals it follows that, if $c_0 = 0$ and all the digits after the point are $c_n = b_n - 1$, then $\alpha = 1$.

In fact, then

$$s_n = 1 - \frac{1}{b_1 b_2 \ldots b_n},$$

and 1 is the least upper bound of all s_n's. Otherwise, should there be another least upper bound $\alpha < 1$, we would then have

$$0 < 1 - \alpha < \frac{1}{b_1 b_2 \ldots b_n} < \frac{1}{2^n}$$

for all indices n, which is a contradiction.

Again, we agree to exclude Cantor expansions in which starting from some place after the point all the consecutive digits c_n are $b_n - 1$. By repeating all arguments concerning decimals we prove the following:

Theorem on Cantor Expansion. *Given an infinite sequence of scales* $b_1, b_2, \ldots$ *with* $b_n \geq 2$ *for all n, every real number has one and only one Cantor expansion. The digits for the number* α *are determined by the algorithm*

$$c_0 = [\alpha]$$

If $c_0 = \alpha$, *stop. If* $c_0 < \alpha$, *put*

$$\rho_1 = \alpha - c_0$$

then

$$c_1 = [b_1 \rho_1]$$

If $c_n = b_n \rho_n$, *stop. If* $c_n < b_n \rho_n$, *put*

$$\rho_{n+1} = b_n \rho_n - c_n$$

then

$$c_{n+1} = [b_{n+1} \rho_{n+1}]$$

The algorithm implies

(9) $\rho_n = b_{n-1} b_{n-2} \ldots b_2 b_1 \alpha - [b_{n-1} b_{n-2} \ldots b_2 b_1 \alpha]$,

(10) $c_n = [b_n b_{n-1} \ldots b_2 b_1 \alpha] - b_n [b_{n-1} b_{n-2} \ldots b_2 b_1 \alpha]$

The partial sums s_n satisfy the inequalities

(11) $0 \leq \alpha - s_{n+1} \leq \alpha - s_n < 1/b_1 b_2 \ldots b_n$

The proof of this theorem differs from that for decimals only in that 10^n is replaced by $b_n b_{n-1} \ldots b_2 b_1$, and d_n is replaced by c_n.

A test for rationality, analogous to that for decimals, does not hold for Cantor expansion. Here is a counterexample. Let the scale-sequence be

$$b_1 = 2, \quad b_2 = 3, \quad \ldots, \quad b_n = n + 1$$

Let $c_0 = 2$, and let all other digits $c_n = 1$. Thus the Cantor expansion is $2\dot{\ }111\ldots$, it is "periodic" and represents the number e, known in mathematics as the base of the natural logarithms (see page 8). The number e is irrational; in fact, the equation $e = m/n$ is contradicted by formula (10):

$$1 = \left[2\cdot3 \ldots (n-1)\, n(n+1)\, \frac{m}{n} \right]$$

$$- (n+1) \left[2\cdot3 \ldots (n-1)n\, \frac{m}{n} \right] = 0$$

The very concept of periodicity cannot be translated literally in Cantor expansion. However, *sufficient* conditions are known for a Cantor expansion to represent an irrational number. For example, if each prime number divides infinitely many of the b_n's and the Cantor expansion is infinite, then it represents an irrational number. In fact, should α be rational, r/s, take in formula (10) the index n such that the product $b_1 b_2 \ldots b_n$ be divisible by s. Then formula (10) would imply that starting from the nth place, i.e., for $m > n$,

$$c_m = \left[b_m b_{m-1} \ldots b_2 b_1\, \frac{r}{s} \right] = b_m \left[b_{m-1} b_{m-2} \ldots b_2 b_1\, \frac{r}{s} \right] = 0,$$

contrary to the assumption that the expansion is infinite.

However, this condition is *not* necessary. For example, let

$$b_1 = 2, \quad b_2 = 3, \quad b_3 = 5, \quad \ldots, \quad b_n = p_n$$

i.e., b_n is the nth *prime* number, and let all the digits $c_n = 1$. Then the Cantor expansion in that scale sequence is $0\dot{\ }111\ldots$ and represents the number

$$\varepsilon = \frac{1}{p_1} + \frac{1}{p_1 p_2} + \ldots + \frac{1}{p_1 p_2 \ldots p_n} + \ldots$$

Each prime divides only one of the b_n's, and the Cantor expansion is infinite. However, we shall prove that the number ε is irrational. Suppose, to the contrary, that $\varepsilon = r/q$. Take a sufficiently large prime p_n such that

(i) $$q \leq p_{n-1} < p_n$$

Formula (10) would give

(ii) $$1 = \left[p_1 p_2 \cdots p_{n-1} p_n \frac{r}{q} \right] - p \left[p_1 p_2 \cdots p_{n-1} \frac{r}{q} \right]$$

Decompose the natural q into prime factors. Should all the factors of q occur in the first power only, the equality (ii) would give the contradiction $1 = 0$. Should some prime factors of q occur with exponent higher than 1, write

$$p_n p_{n-1} \cdots p_2 p_1 \frac{r}{q} = A + \frac{a}{s}$$

$$p_{n-1} \cdots p_2 p_1 \frac{r}{q} = B + \frac{b}{s}$$

with natural numbers A and B, and

$$1 \leq a < s, \quad 1 \leq b < s.$$

There must be

(iii) $$2s < q$$

because in formula (ii) not all primes would cancel with the prime factors of q.

Thus, formula (ii) would give

(iv) $$1 = A - p_n B$$

On the other hand, as the result of the same operations performed on the same numbers, the two numbers

$$A + \frac{a}{s} \quad \text{and} \quad p_n \left(B + \frac{b}{s} \right)$$

without brackets are equal. Comparing them and using (iii) we get

(v) $$p_n = \frac{a + s}{b}$$

Since we suppose

$$1 \leq a < s \quad \text{and} \quad 1 \leq b < s$$

we have

$$a + s < 2s \quad \text{and a fortiori} \quad \frac{a + s}{b} < 2s$$

As a result, formula (iv) gives $p_n < 2s$. However, $2s \leq q$, and so $p_n < q$, contradictory to the initial assumption (i). Thus, the number ε is irrational.

The Cantor expansion of a given number depends essentially on the base-sequence chosen. A suitable choice may be useful in examining the arithmetical structure of a given number.

It is worth noticing that one can choose such a base-sequence that every rational number will have only a finite Cantor expansion. To do this all the consecutive prime numbers are arranged into a sequence, $p_1, p_2, \ldots$, followed by their squares, cubes, and the consecutive powers. Now, take the base sequence as follows: $b_1 = p_1$, $b_2 = p_2$, $b_3 = p_1^2$, $b_4 = p_1^3$, and so on, as indicated by the arrows in Table 1.

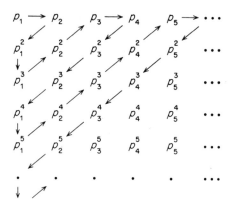

Table 1

The fact that only rational numbers have finite Cantor expansion in this base-sequence follows directly from the very construction.

2. Continued Fraction Expansion

The number represented in continued fraction expansion is also approximated by rationals. But no scale is used; instead of the partial sums, we form another sequence of rationals.

Consider a sequence $a_0 : a_1 a_2 \ldots$. An integer a_0, appears before the colon, and a finite or infinite sequence or natural digits $a_n \geq 1$ follows the colon. The following sequence of rationals is formed by addition and division:

$$(1) \qquad f_0 = a_0, \quad f_1 = a_0 + \frac{1}{a_1}, \quad f_2 = a_0 + \frac{1}{a_1 + (1/a_2)}, \quad \ldots$$

The sequence (1), denoted later by $a_0 : a_1 a_2 \ldots$, is called a *continued fraction*. The f_n's are called its *convergents*.

In more general continued fractions the 1 in the numerators is replaced by any integer or, still more generally, by any real number. The continued fraction defined here is called *simple*. We will deal only with simple continued fractions.

Before showing how a continued fraction represents a real number we will prove the following:

Arithmetical Rules for Continued Fractions. *The convergents are rational numbers $f_n = p_n/q_n$ in which*

$$(2) \qquad \begin{aligned} p_0 &= a_0, \quad p_1 = a_0 a_1 + 1, \quad p_n = p_{n-1} a_n + p_{n-2}, \\ q_0 &= 1, \quad\;\; q_1 = a_1, \qquad\qquad q_n = q_{n-1} a_n + q_{n-2} \end{aligned}$$

$$(3) \qquad q_n p_{n-1} - q_{n-1} p_n = (-1)^n$$

$$(4) \qquad q_n p_{n-2} - q_{n-2} p_n = (-1)^{n-1} a_n$$

(5)   *Every convergent p_n/q_n is in its lowest terms*

(6)   *The convergents with even indices, f_{2k}, increase with k, and the convergents with odd indices, f_{2l+1}, decrease with l*

(7)   *Any convergent with an even index is less than any with odd index,*

$$f_{2k} < f_{2l+1}$$

(8)   *All denominators $q_n \geq 2^{(n-1)/2}$*

Proof. Formulae (2) follow by induction. For $n = 2$ and $n = 3$ they are true by definition (1). Assuming them true for n; i.e., assuming that

(9)
$$\frac{p_n}{q_n} = \frac{p_{n-1}a_n + p_{n-2}}{q_{n-1}a_n + q_{n-2}}$$

we must prove that (9) holds for $n + 1$. In fact, by definition

$$\frac{p_n}{q_n} = a_0 + \cfrac{1}{a_1 + \ldots + (1/a_n)}$$

and

$$\frac{p_{n+1}}{q_{n+1}} = a_0 + \cfrac{1}{a_1 + \ldots + \cfrac{1}{a_n + (1/a_{n+1})}}$$

which shows that in order to obtain p_{n+1}/q_{n+1}, we can replace a_n whenever it occurs, by $a_n + (1/a_{n+1})$. Since the digit a_n does not occur in

$$p_{n-1}, \quad p_{n-2}, \quad q_{n-1}, \quad q_{n-2}$$

we have by (9)

$$\frac{p_{n+1}}{q_{n+1}} = \frac{p_{n-1}[a_n + (1/a_{n+1})] + p_{n-2}}{q_{n-1}[a_n + (1/a_{n+1})] + q_{n-2}} = \frac{(p_{n-1}a_n + p_{n-2})a_{n+1} + p_{n-1}}{(q_{n-1}a_n + q_{n-2})a_{n+1} + q_{n-1}}$$

which by the inductive hypothesis (9) proves formulae (2).

Formula (3) is proved as follows. By (2) we have

$$q_n p_{n-1} - q_{n-1} p_n = (q_{n-1}a_n + q_{n-2})p_{n-1} - q_{n-1}(p_{n-1}a_n + p_{n-2})$$

$$= -(q_{n-1}p_{n-2} - q_{n-2}p_{n-1})$$

This shows that the absolute value of

$$q_n p_{n-1} - q_{n-1} p_n$$

for all indices n is the same but that the signs of the expression alternate. Since

$$q_1 p_0 - q_0 p_1 = -1$$

for $n = 1$, we have the formula (3).

The proof of (4) is analogous. Again, by (2) we have

$$q_n p_{n-2} - q_{n-2} p_n = (q_{n-1} a_n + q_{n-2}) p_{n-2} - q_{n-2}(p_{n-1} a_n + p_{n-2})$$
$$= a_n(q_{n-1} p_{n-2} - q_{n-2} p_{n-1})$$

and the last expression in parentheses is, by (3), equal to $(-1)^{n-1}$.

The proof of (5) follows from (3). In fact, p_n and q_n cannot have any common divisor (greater than 1). Otherwise the right hand side, $(-1)^n$, in (3) would have the same divisor.

The proof of (6) follows from (5), written as

$$f_{n+2} - f_n = \frac{(-1)^n a_{n+2}}{q_n q_{n+2}}$$

If n is even ($n = 2k$), then the right hand side is positive. Thus,

$$f_{2(k+1)} > f_{2k}$$

If n is odd ($n = 2m + 1$), then analogously

$$f_{2m+3} > f_{2m+1}$$

The proof of (7) follows from (3) and (6). Substitute $n = 2h + 1$ into (3) to get

$$f_{2h+1} - f_{2h} = \frac{1}{q_{2h} q_{2h+1}} > 0$$

whence $f_{2h} < f_{2h+1}$ for every natural h. By (6) we may continue this inequality in both directions; viz.,

$$f_{2(h-i)} < \cdots < f_{2(h-1)} < f_{2h} < f_{2h+1} < f_{2(h-1)+1} < \cdots < f_{2(h-j)+1}$$

Substituting $h - i$ for k and $h - j$ for l, we get (7).

Finally, the proof of (8) follows from (2). The equation

$$q_n = q_{n-1} a_n + q_{n-2}$$

shows that, since all digits $a_n \geq 1$, so are all quotients

$$q_n > 2q_{n-2}$$

and, moreover,

$$q_n > q_{n-1}$$

Thus, formula (2) again yields

$$q_n > 2q_{n-2}$$

If n is even, $(n = 2k)$, then $k = n/2$, and we obtain

$$q_{2k} > 2q_{2(k-1)} > \ldots > 2^k q_0 = 2^k$$

Thus, a fortiori $q_n > 2^{(n-1)/2}$.

If n is odd $(n = 2l + 1)$, then $l = (n - 1)/2$, and we obtain

$$q_{2l+1} > 2q_{2(l-1)+1} > \ldots > 2^l q_0 = 2^l$$

Thus, $q_n > 2^{(n-1)/2}$ also. This completes the entire proof.

Properties (6) and (7) are shown geometrically in Figure 2. Compare this with decimal or Cantor expansion, page 20.

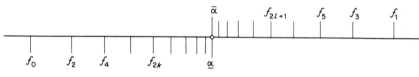

Figure 2

To illustrate the proved arithmetical rules let us calculate the first six convergents of the continued fraction

$$3 : 7(15)1(292)1112 \ldots$$

By (2) we have

$$f_0 = \frac{p_0}{q_0} = \frac{3}{1} = 3$$

$$f_1 = \frac{p_1}{q_1} = \frac{3 \cdot 7 + 1}{7} = \frac{22}{7}$$

$$f_2 = \frac{p_2}{q_2} = \frac{22 \cdot 15 + 3}{7 \cdot 15 + 1} = \frac{333}{106}$$

$$f_3 = \frac{p_3}{q_3} = \frac{333 \cdot 1 + 22}{106 \cdot 1 + 7} = \frac{355}{113}$$

$$f_4 = \frac{p_4}{q_4} = \frac{333 \cdot 292 + 333}{113 \cdot 292 + 106} = \frac{103993}{33102}$$

$$f_5 = \frac{p_5}{q_5} = \frac{103993 \cdot 1 + 335}{33102 + 113} = \frac{104348}{33215}$$

By (5), all these fractions are in their lowest terms. Formulae (6) and (7) can be checked, also.

This example gives the first few digits in the continued fraction expansion of the number π. The general rule for forming the digits for π is not known.

Archimedes, in the third century B.C., found that π was less than 22/7 but greater than 333/106. A. Metius, about A.D. 1600, found that π was between 333/106 and 355/115. The error will be estimated later (see page 39).

From (2) and (9), it follows that the last or $(n + 1)$st convergent of a *finite* continued fraction $a_0 : a_1 a_2 \ldots a_{n-1} a_n 1$ is equal to the last, or nth, convergent of $a_0 : a_1 a_2 \ldots a_{n-1}(a_n + 1)$.

To check this, calculate both convergents by (2) and (9). This allows us to assume that a *finite* continued fraction always has as many "even" as "odd" convergents, since we may, if needed, enlarge the fraction by annexing 1 as an additional last digit, or if 1 is the last digit, by omitting it. Inequality (7) should then be rewritten as

$$f_{2k} \leq f_{2l+1}$$

since equality is possible for the two last convergents of *finite* continued fractions only.

From (7) it follows that for both finite and infinite continued fractions all "even" convergents (f_{2k}) are bounded from above, viz. by any of the "odd" convergents, f_{2l+1}; similarly all the "odd" convergents are bounded from below. By the continuity axiom, there exist a real number $\underline{\alpha}$, which is the least upper bound for all f_{2k}, and a real number $\bar{\alpha}$, which is the greatest lower bound for all f_{2l+1}. We will now prove that $\underline{\alpha} = \bar{\alpha}$

First, let us dispose of the trivial case in which the continued fraction is finite. Our assumption is that the last two convergents are equal, and by (6) one of them is $\underline{\alpha}$ and the other $\bar{\alpha}$. The continuity axiom has not been used here in its full power.

If the continued fraction is infinite, inequality (7) implies that $\underline{\alpha} \leq \bar{\alpha}$. We will show a pedantic proof of this. By our definition (see page 15) of $\underline{\alpha}$ as the least upper bound for all f_{2k}, if any number $\beta < \underline{\alpha}$, there must be some $f_{2k} > \beta$, since $\underline{\alpha}$ is the *least* upper bound. Analogously, if $\gamma > \bar{\alpha}$ there must be some $f_{2l+1} < \gamma$. Should $\underline{\alpha} > \bar{\alpha}$ substitute $\bar{\alpha}$ for β; there must then be some $f_{2k} > \bar{\alpha}$. Now substitute f_{2k} for γ; there must be some $f_{2l+1} < f_{2k}$. But this contradicts (7), which states that $f_{2k} \leq f_{2l+1}$. (Do not be confused by the notation: f_{2k} and f_{2l+1} denote elements of *different* sets.)

Now, since $\underline{\alpha} \leq \bar{\alpha}$, it remains to be proved that the supposition $\underline{\alpha} < \bar{\alpha}$ leads to a contradiction. In fact, we must have $\bar{\alpha} \leq f_{2n+1}$, since $\bar{\alpha}$ is a *lower* bound for all f_{2n+1}. Similarly $f_{2n} \leq \underline{\alpha}$. Thus, $\underline{\alpha} < \bar{\alpha}$ would imply

$$0 < \bar{\alpha} - \underline{\alpha} < f_{2n+1} - f_{2n},$$

and the right-hand expression is, by (4), equal to $1/(q_{2n}q_{2n+1})$ which, in turn, proves by (8) to be less than $1/4^n$. Eventually, we get

$$0 < \bar{\alpha} - \underline{\alpha} < 1/4^n$$

for every n, whence $4^n < 1/(\bar{\alpha} - \underline{\alpha})$. But this contradicts the Archimedean axiom (see pages 9, 21, 27). This completes the proof that $\underline{\alpha} = \bar{\alpha}$.

Thus, every continued fraction $a_0 : a_1 a_2 \ldots$ represents a unique real number α equal to the common least upper bound of all "even" convergents and to the greatest lower bound of all "odd" convergents.

From the geometrical interpretation on page 34 it can be seen that the continued fraction expansion reflects, in a way, both Dedekind's and Cantor's ideas about the concept of a real number (see page 8). The fact that all "even" convergents are less than all the "odd" convergents reflects the idea of Dedekind's cut. The fact that both the "even" and the "odd" convergents tend to the same number reflects Cantor's idea of a real number as a limit of sequences of rationals.

There can be, however, two different continued fractions representing the same number α, as the previous example $[a_0 : a_1 \ldots a_{n-1}1$ and $a_0 : a_1 \ldots a_{n-1}(a_n + 1)]$ shows. Therefore, we agree to *exclude* finite continued fractions with the last digit 1.

This is an agreement analogous with the 9's convention in the decimal expansion or with the $c_n = b_n - 1$ in Cantor expansion. Notice, however, that it applies here to finite expansions only.

With this agreement we will prove the following:

Theorem on Continued Fraction Expansion. *Every real number α has one, and only one, continued fraction expansion for which α is the least* *upper bound of all the "even" convergents, equal to the greatest lower bound of all the "odd" convergents, as defined by* (2).

Given α, the digits are determined by the following algorithm:
Put $\rho_0 = \alpha$, then

$$a_0 = [\rho_0]$$

If $\rho_n = a_n$ *stop. If* $\rho_n > a_n$ *put*

$$\rho_{n+1} = \frac{1}{\rho_n - a_n}$$

then

$$a_{n+1} = [\rho_{n+1}]$$

The algorithm implies

(10)
$$\alpha = \frac{p_{n-1}\rho_n + p_{n-2}}{q_{n-1}\rho_n + q_{n-2}}$$

The real number α *always falls between two consecutive convergents, and*

(11)
$$\left| \alpha - \frac{p_n}{q_n} \right| + \left| \alpha - \frac{p_{n+1}}{q_{n+1}} \right| = \frac{1}{q_n q_{n+1}}$$

The convergents satisfy the following inequalities:

(12)
$$\frac{a_{n+2}}{q_n q_{n+2}} < \left| \alpha - \frac{p_n}{q_n} \right| < \frac{1}{q_n q_{n+1}}$$

(13)
$$\left| \alpha - \frac{p_{n+1}}{q_{n+1}} \right| < \left| \alpha - \frac{p_n}{q_n} \right|$$

Before proving the Theorem let us comment on it.

First, here are two examples illustrating the algorithm for determining the digits.

Example 1. Let $\alpha = 779/207$. Then $a_0 = [779/207]$. To obtain this carry out the division $\rho_0 = 3 + 158/207$ so that $a_0 = 3 < \rho_0$. Put

$$\rho_1 = \frac{1}{\rho_0 - a_0} = \frac{1}{158/207} = \frac{207}{158} = 1 + \frac{49}{158}$$

Then $a_1 = 1 < \rho_1$. Put

$$\rho_2 = \frac{1}{\rho_1 - a_1} = \frac{158}{49} = 3 + \frac{11}{49}$$

Then $a_2 = 3 < \rho_2$. Put

$$\rho_3 = \frac{1}{\rho_2 - a_2} = \frac{49}{11} = 4 + \frac{5}{11}$$

Then $a_3 = 4 < \rho_3$. Put

$$\rho_4 = \frac{1}{\rho_3 - a_3} = \frac{11}{5} = 2 + \frac{1}{5}$$

Then $a_4 = 2 < \rho_4$. Put

$$\rho_5 = \frac{5}{1} = 5$$

Thus, $a_5 = 5 = \rho_5$. Stop. The continued fraction is $3:13425$, and it is finite.

The algorithm is, thus, the same as *Euclid's algorithm* for finding the greatest common divisor of two integers. This continued fraction may be written explicitly as

$$3 + \cfrac{1}{1 + \cfrac{1}{3 + \cfrac{1}{4 + \cfrac{1}{2 + \cfrac{1}{5}}}}}$$

ρ_3 may be written explicitly as

$$\rho_3 = 4 + \frac{1}{2 + (1/5)}$$

We notice that ρ_3 represents the *remainder* of the continued fraction after the digits a_0, a_1, a_2 have been deleted.

More generally, if $a_0:a_1a_2 \ldots a_n a_{n+1} \ldots$ is a continued fraction, then ρ_n is $a_n:a_{n+1}a_{n+2}\ldots$. The same idea is expressed in formula (10).

By means of formula (2) we calculate all the convergents:

$$f_0 = \frac{3}{1}, \quad f_1 = \frac{4}{1}, \quad f_2 = \frac{15}{4}, \quad f_3 = \frac{64}{17}, \quad f_4 = \frac{143}{38}, \quad f_5 = \frac{779}{207} = \alpha.$$

If we take the convergent f_2 instead of α, then by formula (12) the error is estimated as

$$\left| \frac{779}{207} - \frac{15}{4} \right| < \frac{1}{4.207}$$

which is less than .0013 or .05 per cent of the approximated number $779/207$. Comparison with Example 2 on page 22 shows that the decimal approximation $3.7 = 37/10$ of the same number α has a *greater denominator* $(10 > 4)$ but is *less accurate* than the approximation by continued fraction $(15/4)$.

Example 2. Let $\alpha = \sqrt{2}$. By the algorithm put $\rho_0 = \sqrt{2}$. Then

$$a_0 = [\sqrt{2}] = 1 < \rho_0$$

Put

$$\rho_1 = \frac{1}{\rho_0 - a_0} = \frac{1}{\sqrt{2} - 1} = \sqrt{2} + 1$$

Then
$$a_1 = [\sqrt{2} + 1] = 2 < \rho_1$$
Put
$$\rho_2 = \frac{1}{\rho_1 - a_1} = \sqrt{2} + 1$$

Then $a_2 = 2$, and the process repeats itself. The continued fraction for $\sqrt{2}$ is $1:22\ldots$. It is *periodic*. Since we have all the digits we can calculate the consecutive convergents by formula (2).

If we take the convergent $f_3 = 17/12$ instead of $\alpha = \sqrt{2}$, then by formula (12) the error is estimated as less than $1/12.39$ which is less than .003; i.e., about 2 per cent of the approximated number $\sqrt{2}$. Comparing that with Example 3 on page 23 shows again that the third decimal approximation $(1.41 = 141/100)$ of $\sqrt{2}$ has a denominator greater than that of the third convergent, but it is less accurate.

Let us now illustrate formula (12) by the example with the number π (see pages 22, 35). For Archimedes' approximation (22/7) the error is less than $1/742$, which is less than .0014 or about .05 per cent of π. Metius' approximation has an error less than $1/113.33102$, which is less than .00000027 or about .00001 per cent of π. Comparison with the data given by decimal expansion of π, page 22, shows again that continued fractions approximate better than decimals.

Formula (13) shows that the error of the approximation always decreases with index n. In this respect, continued fractions approximate *faster* than decimals (compare page 22).

Proof of the theorem. That a continued fraction $a_0 : a_1 a_2 \ldots$ represents a *unique* real number α follows from the uniqueness of the least upper bound of a bounded set, and from the proved equality $\underline{\alpha} = \bar{\alpha}$. That a real number has a unique continued fraction $a_0 : a_1 a_2 \ldots$ follows from the algorithm determining uniquely the digits. However, we must prove also that the continued fraction obtained by the algorithm does represent the given number α. If α is rational, p/q, the algorithm is finite. In fact, put $\rho_0 = p/q$. Then

$$a_0 = [p/q]$$

If p/q is an integer, stop. If not, that is, if $p/q > a_0$, put

$$p/q = a_0 + 1/\rho_1$$

The remainder ρ_1 is *rational*, say r_1/q with $0 < r_1 < q$. Then,

$$a_2 = [r_2/r_1]$$

Proceeding in this way, we get

$$0 < r_{m+1} < r_m < \ldots < r_2 < r_1 < q$$

But, there is only a finite number of naturals r less than q, and thus the algorithm stops at some $(m + 1)$st step, where

$$\rho_{m+1} = [\rho_{m+1}] = a_{m+1}$$

Then, formulae (9) and (10) show that α is equal to the last convergent of the finite continued fraction $a_0 : a_1 a_2 \ldots a_m a_{m+1}$.

For rational α this procedure is known as *Euclid's algorithm*. A numerical example was given on page 38.

If α is irrational, the algorithm gives an *infinite* continued fraction $a_0 : a_1 a_2 \ldots$. In order to prove that it represents the number α, take the "even" convergents f_{2k} and consider the difference $\alpha - f_{2k}$. By (10), (9), and (3) we get

$$\alpha - f_{2k} = \frac{1}{(q_{2k}\rho_{2k+1} + q_{2k-1})q_{2k}} > 0$$

By (8) all the $q_n \geq 2^{(n-1)/2}$, and by the algorithm all $\rho_n > 1$. Hence it follows that for all indices k

$$0 < \alpha - f_{2k} < 1/4^{k-1}$$

Since $1/4^{k-1}$ can be made smaller than any given fixed positive number, by taking k sufficiently large, the last inequality proves that α is the least upper bound of all f_{2k} and thus $a_0 : a_1 a_2 \ldots$ represents α.

The proof of (11) follows directly from (6), (7), and (3). In fact, if n is even $(2k)$, the left-hand side of (11) is

$$\alpha - \frac{p_{2k}}{q_{2k}} + \frac{p_{2k+1}}{q_{2k+1}} - \alpha = \frac{1}{q_{2k}q_{2k+1}}$$

If n is odd $(2k + 1)$, then the left-hand side of (11) is the same. Thus (11) holds for any n.

The proof of the right-hand side of inequality (12) follows directly from (11). The left-hand side of the inequality

$$\left| \alpha - \frac{p_n}{q_n} \right| > \frac{a_{n+2}}{q_n q_{n+2}}$$

follows by (6), (7), and (4). In fact, if n is even $(2k)$, then

$$\alpha > f_{2k+2} > f_{2k}$$

whence

$$\alpha - f_{2k} > f_{2k+2} - f_{2k} = \frac{a_{2k+2}}{q_{2k} q_{2k+2}}$$

by (4). If n is odd $(2k + 1)$, then

$$\alpha < f_{2k+1} < f_{2k+3}$$

whence

$$\alpha - f_{2k+1} < f_{2k+1} - f_{2k+3} < \frac{-a_{2k+3}}{q_{2k+1} q_{2k+3}}$$

again by (4).

The proof of (13) follows from (12). In fact, since

$$a_{n+2} \geq 1 \quad \text{and} \quad q_n < q_{n+1}$$

the left-hand side of inequality (12) implies

$$\left| \alpha - \frac{p_n}{q_n} \right| > \frac{1}{q_{n+1} q_{n+2}}$$

and now the right-hand side of inequality (12) implies

$$\frac{1}{q_{n+1} q_{n+2}} > \left| \alpha - \frac{p_{n+1}}{q_{n+1}} \right|$$

This completes the whole proof of the theorem.

If α is rational, formulae (11), (12), and (13) are valid only for the finite number of convergents.

Inequality (12) implies that

(14)
$$\frac{1}{(q_n + q_{n+1}) q_n} < \left| \alpha - \frac{p_n}{q_n} \right| < \frac{1}{q_n^2}$$

In fact, the right-hand side estimate follows from $q_{n+1} \geq q_n$. The left-hand side estimate follows from $a_{n+2} \geq 1$ and (2)

$$\frac{a_{n+2}}{q_{n+2}} = \frac{1}{q_{n+1} + (q_n/a_{n+2})} \geq \frac{1}{q_{n+1} + q_n}$$

Whereas the left-hand side of (14) shows how *close* a convergent p_n/q_n can be to α, the right-hand side shows that the convergent cannot be *too close* to α. Although the Theorem on Continued Fraction Expansion holds for both rational and irrational numbers, its real importance is for irrational numbers, as can be seen from the following theorem.

Test for Rationality. *A number is rational if and only if its continued fraction is finite.*

Proof. That if a continued fraction is finite it represents a rational number follows by the very definition of the continued fraction. That a continued fraction is finite if it represents a rational number follows by Euclid's algorithm.

This Test implies that a number is *irrational* if and only if its continued fraction is *infinite*. In this respect, the continued fraction expansion reflects better the arithmetical structure of the number represented than other expansions, like decimal or Cantor's. Compare page 25. The continued fraction expansion represents a rational number by using only *finite* sequences of digits, whereas infinite sequences represent irrational numbers only. Moreover, the continued fraction expansion allows us to identify among the irrational numbers those which are algebraic of degree 2; i.e., those which satisfy a quadratic equation with rational coefficients (see page 9). This fact is expressed by the

Theorem on Periodic Continued Fractions. *An irrational number is algebraic of degree 2 if and only if its continued fraction is periodic.*

Proof. If the continued fraction is periodic starting from some place; i.e., if

$$\alpha = a_0 : a_1 \ldots a_k \bar{a}_1 \ldots \bar{a}_m \bar{a}_1 \ldots \bar{a}_m$$

consider its purely periodic part

$$\rho = 0 : \bar{a}_1 \ldots \bar{a}_m \bar{a}_1 \ldots$$

that is the kth remainder of α. By formula (10)

$$\alpha = \frac{p_k \rho + p_{k-1}}{q_k \rho + q_{k-1}}$$

Since the mth remainder of ρ is again ρ (periodicity), the same formula (10) gives

$$\rho = \frac{\bar{p}_m \rho + \bar{p}_{m-1}}{\bar{q}_m \rho + \bar{q}_{m-1}}$$

Now we express ρ in terms of α and get a *quadratic* equation for α with rational coefficients of integer p's and q's. Thus, α is algebraic of degree 2.

To be pedantic, we must prove that the equation cannot be of the first order. Otherwise α would be rational, and its continued fraction would be finite, not periodic, as assumed.

The second part of the proof is more intricate. Let the real number α satisfy the quadratic equation

$$A\alpha^2 + B\alpha + C = 0$$

with integer coefficients, A, B, and C. Expand α into a continued fraction

$$a_0 : a_1 \ldots a_n a_{n+1} \ldots$$

We must prove its periodicity. Let p_n/q_n be its convergents, and let ρ_n be its nth remainder, for which formula (10) holds. We substitute (10) into the quadratic equation, and after appropriate (rather lengthy) calculations we find that ρ_n satisfies another quadratic equation

$$A_n \rho_n^2 + B_n \rho_n + C_n = 0$$

and that its integer coefficients satisfy the identies:

$$A_n = A p_{n-1}^2 + B p_{n-1} q_{n-1} + C q_{n-1}^2$$

$$C_n = A_{n-1}$$

$$B_n^2 - 4A_n C_n = B^2 - 4AC$$

In order to prove periodicity of the expansion we shall show that all the coefficients, A_n, B_n, and C_n are bounded by fixed numbers independent of n. Then, A_n, B_n, and C_n, being integers, can assume only a finite number of values, and the collection of quadratic equations for p_n is finite. Consequently, the choice of digits a_n is also finite, since they are expressed by the algorithm through the p_n's. Thus, finally, the digits must repeat themselves; i.e., the continued fraction is periodic.

In order to prove that A_n, B_n, and C_n are bounded, it is enough to prove that only the A_n's are bounded. Then, by the third identity for the coefficients, $C_n = A_{n-1}$ and the B_n's will also be bounded.

To prove that the A_n's are bounded we first conclude from inequality (14) that

$$|q_{n-1}(q_{n-1}\alpha - p_{n-1})| < 1.$$

Denote

$$q_{n-1}(q_{n-1}\alpha - p_{n-1}) = \delta_n$$

Thus,

$$|\delta_n| < 1 \quad \text{and} \quad p_{n-1} = q_{n-1}\alpha - (\delta_n/q_{n-1})$$

Substitute p_{n-1} into the expression for A_n to get

$$A_n = (A\alpha^2 + B\alpha + C)q_{n-1}^2 - (2A\alpha + B)\delta_n + (A\,\delta_n^2/q_{n-1}^2)$$

The first term on the right-hand side vanishes, since α satisfies the quadratic equation by assumption. We will now estimate the absolute value $|A_n|$. On the right-hand side we apply $|\delta_n| < 1$, the triangle inequality for absolute values (see page 14) and the inequality $1/q_{n-1}^2 < 1$ then the inequality reduces finally to

$$|A_n| < |2A\alpha + B| + |A|$$

Thus all $|A_n|$ are bounded by a fixed number independent of the index n. This completes the whole proof.

Let $\gamma = 0\colon 111\ldots$. Hence

$$\gamma = \cfrac{1}{1 + \gamma}$$

and, therefore,

$$\gamma^2 + \gamma - 1 = 0$$

This equation has the two roots $\frac{1}{2}(\pm\sqrt{5} - 1)$. We will use the positive root, since $\gamma > 0$, and thus

$$\gamma = \frac{1}{2}(\sqrt{5} - 1)$$

The ancient Greeks called γ the "golden number." It satisfies the proportion

$$1:\gamma = \gamma:(1 - \gamma)$$

which divides a segment into two parts such that the whole is as many times longer than one part as that part is longer than the other. The role, if any, of the "golden number" in such areas as aesthetics has been the subject of much speculation.

The test of rationality for continued fractions may be considered as a particular case of a more general situation. Formula (10) allows us to divide all irrational numbers into equivalence classes in the following way: To each class belong numbers which have at some point in their continued fractions, like sequences of digits; for example, 4:231652 ... and 7:291652 .... Hence, it follows that this relation of equivalence is reflexive, symmetric, and transitive (see page 10). Formula (10) implies that if two numbers, α and α', are equivalent, then starting from some place there are

$$\alpha = \frac{p_{n-1}\rho_n + p_{n-2}}{q_{n-1}\rho_n + q_{n-2}}$$

and

$$\alpha' = \frac{p'_{n-1}\rho_n + p'_{n-2}}{q'_{n-1}\rho_n + q'_{n-2}}$$

The first convergents p/q and p'/q' may differ, but the remainders ρ_n do not. By eliminating ρ_n, we obtain

(15)
$$\alpha' = \frac{K\alpha + L}{M\alpha + N}$$

A direct calculation, with the use of (3), shows that the integers K, L, M, N satisfy the condition

(15')
$$KN - LM = \pm 1$$

It can be proved[1] that, conversely, if two numbers α and α' are connected by the relationship (15) with the condition (15'), then α and α' are equivalent.

In particular, all quadratic algebraic numbers which have the same period in their continued fractions are equivalent.

The continued fraction expansion is more discerning than the decimal expansion in this sense: If the decimal is finite *or* periodic, it represents a rational number. The continued fraction, if finite, represents a rational number, but, if periodic, indicates not only that the number is irrational but also reveals the quadratic character of the irrationality. Whether and how continued fractions distinguish among irrationals other algebraic numbers of degree higher than 2 is not known.

REFERENCE

(1) G. M. Hardy and E. M. Wright, *An Introduction to the Theory of Numbers.* 3rd ed. (Oxford: The Clarendon Press, 1956) pp. 141–143.

Approximation of Real Numbers by Rationals

In this chapter we shall discuss the accuracy of approximation of real numbers by rationals and the distribution of irrational numbers among the reals.

I. The Best Approximation

In the decimal or Cantor expansions the accuracy of approximation of the number α has been estimated by formulae (6), page 22, and (11), page 28, respectively, as

$$0 \leq \alpha - \frac{r_n}{t_n} < \frac{1}{t_n}$$

with $t_n = 10^n$ for the decimal expansion and $t_n = b_1 b_2 \ldots b_n$ for the Cantor expansion. For continued fractions the accuracy of approximation has been estimated by formula (12), page 37, as

$$\left| \alpha - \frac{p_n}{q_n} \right| < \frac{1}{q_n q_{n+1}}$$

49

Comparison of the right-hand sides of both estimates shows that for rationals with equal denominators the continued fraction approximation is more accurate, because

$$\frac{1}{q_n q_{n+1}} < \frac{1}{q_n}$$

This fact has previously been illustrated by numerical examples. See pages 37–39.

The continued fraction approximation to a real number is *better* than any other rational approximation in the following sense: Any other rational number a/b with the natural denominator b not exceeding q_n is at a distance greater from α than the convergent p_n/q_n. More precisely: *If p_n/q_n is the nth convergent to α then for every rational*

$$a/b \neq p_n/q_n \quad \text{with} \quad 1 \leq b \leq q_n,$$

there is

(1)
$$\left| \alpha - \frac{p_n}{q_n} \right| < \left| \alpha - \frac{a}{b} \right|$$

The proof of this fact will follow from a stronger theorem to be proved on pages 54–58.

Ch. Huyghens in his book *Descriptio Automati Planetarii* (1682) applied that fact in designing toothed gearings for a planetarium. He had to use ratios of transmission taken from celestial observations. Those ratios, however, often had very large denominators (and numerators), and it was technically impossible to construct such gearings. Looking for a rational approximation to the original ratio but with a smaller denominator, Huyghens noticed that the continued fractions were better than others. Compare Example 1, page 37.

The approximation of a real number by convergents of its continued fraction is not only better than by decimals (in the sense specified above), but it is also faster. See page 39.

However, the decimal expansion has the advantage that the sum, difference, product, and quotient of two decimal approximations are always decimal approximations to the sum, difference, product, and quotient, respectively, of the two numbers approximated. This is not true for continued fractions. For example, if f_n is the *n*th convergent to α, and g_n is the *n*th convergent to β, then neither $f_n + g_n$ nor $f_n g_n$ is necessarily a convergent to $\alpha + \beta$ or $\alpha\beta$, respectively.

The converse of the Theorem on Better Approximation is not true. If a rational p/q is *not* a convergent to the real number α, it *can* happen that p/q is an approximation better than others; i.e., for every rational

$$a/b \neq p/q \quad \text{with} \quad 1 \leq b \leq q$$

there *is*

$$|\alpha - p/q| < |\alpha - a/b|$$

Here is an example. Let $\alpha = \frac{1}{5}$, $p = 1$, $q = 3$, so that $p/q = \frac{1}{3}$, which is *not* one of the (only two) convergents: $f_0 = 0, f_1 = \frac{1}{5}$. But, for every rational

$$a/b \neq \tfrac{1}{3} \quad \text{with} \quad 1 \leq b \leq 3$$

there *is*

$$\left| \frac{1}{5} - \frac{1}{3} \right| < \left| \frac{1}{5} - \frac{a}{b} \right|$$

This can be checked as follows. If

$$\frac{2}{15} \geq \left| \frac{1}{5} - \frac{a}{b} \right|$$

for some a/b, then necessarily

$$\frac{1}{5} \leq \frac{a}{b} \leq \frac{1}{3}$$

which, because of $1 \leq b \leq 3$, implies $b = 3$, thus, $a = 1$, contrary to $a/b \neq \frac{1}{3}$.

Thus, a convergent is always a rational approximation better than others, but a rational approximation better than others need not be a convergent. In order to have the implication both ways we introduce the concept of the *best approximation*. *A rational p/q* (with integers $q \geq 1$, p) *is called the best approximation to a real number α if for every rational $a/b \neq p/q$ with $1 \leq b \leq q$ one has*

(2) $$|q\alpha - p| < |b\alpha - a|$$

In the formula on better approximation (1) the *distance* δ' from a rational p/q to the real number α is understood as

$$\delta' = \left| \alpha - \frac{p}{q} \right|$$

whereas in the definition of the best approximation (2), we use a different *distance*

$$\delta = |q\alpha - p|$$

Thus,

$$\delta = q\delta'$$

This can be interpreted geometrically as follows. Take on the plane a coordinate system; Oxy. Consider the straight line given by the equation $y = \alpha x$, which passes through the origin O, and has slope α. Let this *line* represent the real number α. The rationals p/q will be represented as points on that plane with coordinates (q, p). Thus, all rationals are represented by a *lattice* of points with integer coordinates; since we assume $q \geq 1$, this lattice is only on the half-plane with positive abscissae.

The ordinary geometrical distance $\bar{\delta}$ from the point (q, p) of the lattice to the line $y = \alpha x$ is

$$\bar{\delta} = \frac{|q\alpha - p|}{\sqrt{1 + \alpha^2}} = \frac{1}{\sqrt{1 + \alpha^2}} \delta$$

Thus, $\delta = \sqrt{1 + \alpha^2}\, \bar{\delta}$, and, for fixed α, the distance δ of the *best* approximation is proportional to the geometrical distance $\bar{\delta}$.

In order to get a geometrical interpretation of distance δ' of the *better* approximation, we calculate the ordinary geometrical distance $\bar{\delta}'$ from the point $(1, p/q)$ to the straight line $y = \alpha x$. Then

$$\bar{\delta}' = \frac{|\alpha - (p/q)|}{\sqrt{1 + \alpha^2}} = \frac{1}{\sqrt{1 + \alpha^2}} \delta'$$

Thus, $\delta' = \sqrt{1 + \alpha^2}\, \bar{\delta}'$, and, for fixed α, the distance δ' is proportional to the geometrical distance $\bar{\delta}'$.

This shows that δ and δ' are (proportional to) the distances from the line $y = \alpha x$ of two *different* points: δ, used in *best* approximation, is the distance from the line representing the real number α to the lattice point (q, p), whereas δ' is the distance from that line to the point $(1, p/q)$, which is *not* a lattice point. In this geometrical interpretation the point $(1, p/q)$ does *not* represent the number p/q (except for the trivial case $q = 1$). Thus, for measuring the accuracy of approximation, the distance δ of the *best* approximation appears to be more appropriate than the distance δ' used in the approximation "better than others."

This is due to the fact that we use a two-dimensional geometrical interpretation, viz. on the plane. Previously, as shown in Figure 2, when we

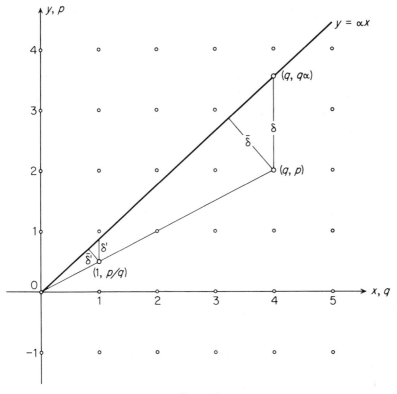

Figure 3

dealt with continued fractions we used a one-dimensional interpretation on the number-axis, which is now shown in Figure 3 as the y-axis.

Thus, to say that p/q is the *best* approximation to the real number α means geometrically that the lattice point (q, p) is closer to the line $y = \alpha x$ than any other point (b, a) with $1 \leq b \leq q$; i.e., than any other lattice point in the strip $1 \leq x \leq q$. The geometrical interpretations of the approximation "better than others" are more cumbersome, involving the distance δ'. Notice that $\delta' \leq \delta$, in any case.

The "best approximation" is always "better than others." In fact, condition (2) implies (1); i.e., if for every rational

$$a/b \neq p/q \quad \text{with} \quad 1 \leq b \leq q$$

inequality (2) holds, then inequality (1) holds also, because

$$\left| \alpha - \frac{p}{q} \right| = \frac{1}{q} |q\alpha - p| < \frac{1}{q} |b\alpha - a| \le \frac{1}{b} |b\alpha - a| = \left| \alpha - \frac{a}{b} \right|$$

However, the converse implication is *not* true; an approximation which is "better than others" need not be the "best." In fact, condition (1) does not necessarily imply (2). Here is a counterexample. Let, again, $\alpha = \frac{1}{5}$, $q = 3$, $p = 1$. We have proved that for every $a/b \ne \frac{1}{3}$ with $1 \le b \le 3$ we have

$$\left| \frac{1}{5} - \frac{1}{3} \right| < \left| \frac{1}{5} - \frac{a}{b} \right|$$

i.e., condition (1) holds. However, condition (2) does not hold for *every* such a/b. In fact, it fails for $a = 0$, $b = 1$, for

$$\left| 3 \cdot \frac{1}{5} - 1 \right| > \left| 1 \cdot \frac{1}{5} - 0 \right|$$

The logical situation is this: If the rational p/q is the *best* approximation to a real number α, then it is also an approximation "better than others." Therefore, if we prove that the convergents are the best approximations, the theorem on better approximation will follow. See page 50. However, the converse of the Theorem on Better Approximation does not hold. Here is a theorem which gives the implication both ways.

Theorem on the Best Approximation. *A rational with a denominator not exceeding $q \ge 1$ is the best approximation to a real number α if, and only if, that rational is one of the convergents p_n/q_n to α, with $q_n \le q$ for $n \ge 1$.*

Before proving the theorem let us comment on it. So far, we have two separate concepts. The first was the convergent of a continued fraction of a number α, and the second was the best (rational) approximation to α. The definition of the best approximation does not make the concept meaningful unless we prove that the defined thing exists, which means that the conditions imposed by the definition on the best approximation are consistent; i.e., not contradictory. The significance of the theorem consists in proving this existence by showing that the best approximations are the convergents. Moreover, the theorem says that there are no other best approximations but the convergents. Therefore we may say both: the *best* approximation and *the* best approximation. This is due to the fact that we use as the distance from a rational p/q to the real number α the expression $|q\alpha - p|$ and not $|\alpha - p/q|$, for which the theorem would fail.

Proof. In order to prove sufficiently ("if") let p_n/q_n be the nth convergent to α. We must prove that for every rational

$$a/b \neq p_n/q_n \quad \text{with} \quad 1 \leq b \leq q_n,$$

there is

(i) $$|q_n\alpha - p_n| < |b\alpha - a|$$

We first prove that inequality (i) holds if

$$a/b = p_{n-1}/q_{n-1} \quad (\neq p_n/q_n)$$

This follows from formula (12), page 37, written separately as

$$|q_n\alpha - p_n| < 1/q_{n+1}$$

and

$$1/q_{n+1} \leq a_{n+1}/q_{n+1} < |q_{n-1}\alpha - p_{n-1}|$$

If

$$\frac{a}{b} \neq \frac{p_{n-1}}{q_{n-1}}$$

then

$$|aq_{n-1} - bp_{n-1}| \geq 1$$

By the triangle inequality for absolute values we have then

$$\left|\frac{a}{b} - \alpha\right| + \left|\alpha - \frac{p_{n-1}}{q_{n-1}}\right| \geq \left|\frac{a}{b} - \frac{p_{n-1}}{q_{n-1}}\right| \geq \frac{1}{bq_{n-1}}$$

whence

$$q_{n-1}|b\alpha - a| + b|q_{n-1}\alpha - p_{n-1}| \geq 1$$

On the other hand, by formula (11) (§ 2, Ch. 2) and by the assumption that $q_n \geq b$, we have that

$$1 = q_n|q_{n-1}\alpha - p_{n-1}| + q_{n-1}|q_n\alpha - p_n|$$
$$\geq b|q_{n-1}\alpha - p_{n-1}| + q_{n-1}|q_n\alpha - p_n|$$

Combining the last two inequalities yields

$$|q_n\alpha - p_n| \le |b\alpha - a|$$

Thus, in order to get (i), it is enough to prove that the equality

$$|q_n\alpha - p_n| = |b\alpha - a|$$

is impossible.

In fact, if α is irrational, the equality

$$q_n\alpha - p_n = \pm(b\alpha - a)$$

implies either $q_n = b$ and $p_n = a$, contrary to

$$\frac{a}{b} \ne \frac{p_n}{q_n}$$

as assumed, or

$$\alpha = \frac{p_n + a}{q_n + b}$$

contrary to the irrationality of α assumed. If α is rational, that equality also proves to be impossible.

Here is a detailed demonstration of that. If p_n/q_n is the last convergent to the (rational) α, then that equality implies

$$0 = |q_n\alpha - p_n| = |b\alpha - a|$$

Hence $\alpha = a/b = p_n/q_n$, contrary to assumption. If p_n/q_n is not the last convergent, let $\alpha = p_N/q_N$ be the last one. Then the equality

$$|q_n\alpha - p_n| = |b\alpha - a|$$

would imply either

$$(q_n - b)p_N = (p_n - a)q_N$$

or

$$(q_n + b)p_N = (p_n + a)q_N$$

In the first case, since p_N and q_N have no common divisor, it would follow that the integer number $q_n - b$ is divisible by $q_N > q_n$, whence

$$q_n = b \quad \text{and} \quad p_n = a$$

contrary to the assumption. In the other case, $q_n + b$ would be divisible by $q_N > q_n$, and hence

$$q_n + b > 2q_n$$

which contradicts the assumption that $b \le q_n$.

In the second part ("only if") we must prove that, if the rational p/q is the best approximation to α; i.e., if for every other rational $a/b \neq p/q$, with $1 \leq b \leq q$, there is

(ii) $$|q\alpha - p| < |b\alpha - a|$$

then p/q must be one of the convergents p_n/q_n to α.

We first prove that

$$p_0/q_0 \leq p/q \leq p_1/q_1$$

In fact, should $p/q < p_0/q_0$ then, in view of $\alpha > p_0/q_0$, we would have that

$$|q_0\alpha - p_0| = |\alpha - p_0| < \left|\alpha - \frac{p}{q}\right| \leq |q\alpha - p|$$

contrary to (ii). And, should it happen that $p/q > p_1/q_1$, then

$$|pq_1 - qp_1| \geq 1$$

Thus, in view of $\alpha < p_1/q_1$, there would be

$$\left|\alpha - \frac{p}{q}\right| > \left|\frac{p_1}{q_1} - \frac{p}{q}\right| \geq \frac{1}{qq_1}$$

whence

$$|q\alpha - p| > \frac{1}{q_1} = |q_0\alpha - p_0|$$

again contrary to (ii).

If p/q is equal to either p_0/q_0 or p_1/q_1, the proof is finished. If not, suppose that p/q is not one of the successive convergents. Then, p/q would have to be between two convergents p_{n-1}/q_{n-1} and p_{n+1}/q_{n+1}, both of which are on the same side of α. This would imply

$$\left|\frac{p}{q} - \frac{p_{n-1}}{q_{n-1}}\right| < \left|\frac{p_n}{q_n} - \frac{p_{n-1}}{q_{n-1}}\right| < \frac{1}{q_n q_{n-1}}$$

and since, supposedly, $p/q \neq p_{n-1}/q_{n-1}$, then

$$\left|\frac{p}{q} - \frac{p_{n-1}}{q_{n-1}}\right| \geq \frac{1}{qq_{n-1}}$$

and we would get that $1 \leq q_n \leq q$. On the other hand, the same supposition would imply

$$\left|\alpha - \frac{p}{q}\right| \geq \left|\frac{p_{n+1}}{q_{n+1}} - \frac{p}{q}\right| \geq \frac{1}{qq_{n+1}}$$

whence, in view of

$$\frac{1}{q_{n+1}} > |q_n\alpha - p_n|$$

we would get

$$|q_n\alpha - p_n| < |q\alpha - p|$$

contrary to (ii).

This completes the entire proof except for one detail: We assumed in the theorem that $n \geq 1$; i.e., we did not claim the theorem to be true for $n = 0$. In fact, the theorem fails for $n = 0$, as the following example shows: Let $\alpha = p_0 + \frac{1}{2}$ with any integer p_0. The 0th convergent of α is p_0. But, it is *not* the best approximation, because there is another best, viz. $a/b = (p_0 + 1)/1$. However, this exception is trivial.

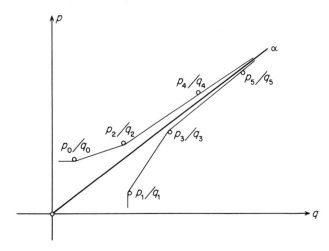

Figure 4

The Theorem on the Best Approximation allows the following geometrical interpretation of a continued fraction, given by F. Klein.[1] If the number α is represented by a straight line $y = \alpha x$, the best approximation to α with a denominator not exceeding $q \geq 1$ is represented by that point (q_n, p_n) of the lattice in the strip $1 \leq x \leq q$, which is *closest* to that line. Imagine that at every lattice point there is a peg. If α is rational y/x, in its lowest term then a stretched string joining the pegs at $(0, 0)$ and (x, y) will not touch any other pegs. If the string is stretched taut with its free end at the peg $(1, 0)$, it will press against the pegs nearest to the line representing α and below it. By the Theorem on Best Approximation, these pegs are at the lattice points representing the "even" convergents to α, viz. at (q_0, p_0), (q_2, p_2), (q_4, p_4), etc. If the free end of the string is held at $(0, 1)$, it will press against the pegs at (q_1, p_1), (q_3, p_3), etc. representing the "odd" convergents to α. If α is irrational the idea is the same, provided that we have an infinite string and know how to fix its end to the peg at infinity. There are also other known geometrical interpretations of continued fractions; for example, by circles.[2]

The Theorem on the Best Approximation leads to the problem how to recognize whether a rational p/q is one of the convergents to a given real number α. Here is a simple

Test for a Convergent. *If the integers $q \geq 1$ and p satisfy the condition*

$$(3) \qquad\qquad |q\alpha - p| < 1/2q$$

then p/q is one of the convergents to α.

Proof. It is enough to prove that p/q is the best approximation to α. Should it not be, let $a/b \neq p/q$ be the best, so that for $1 \leq b \leq q$, let

$$|b\alpha - a| < |q\alpha - p| < 1/2q$$

This would imply

$$\left| \alpha - \frac{a}{b} \right| < \frac{1}{2bq} \quad \text{and} \quad \left| \alpha - \frac{p}{q} \right| < \frac{1}{2q^2}$$

whence

$$\left| \frac{p}{q} - \frac{a}{b} \right| = \left| \left(\frac{p}{q} - \alpha \right) + \left(\alpha - \frac{a}{b} \right) \right| \leq \left| \alpha - \frac{p}{q} \right| + \left| \alpha - \frac{a}{b} \right| < \frac{1}{2bq} + \frac{1}{2q^2}$$

thus,

$$|bp - aq| < (b + q)/2q$$

But $a/b \neq p/q$ implies

$$|bp - aq| \geq 1$$

Therefore

$$(b + q)/2q > 1$$

whence $b > q$, contrary to $b \leq q$, as assumed.

The condition is *not* necessary, as the counterexample shows: Let $\alpha = 779/207$, $q = 1$, $p = 3$. The condition is *not* satisfied, but $3/1$ *is* one of the convergents to α. Compare page 37, Example 1.

2. Universal Law of Approximation

So far, when discussing the best rational approximation to a real number α, we have been keeping α fixed in the argument. Now we want to determine how *good* a best approximation can be for *various* numbers α and the best possible rational approximation guaranteed for every real number α.

Before we examine the problems, let us state them more precisely. First, we will eliminate rationals α, because their last convergent, which is exactly equal to α, is the ultimate best approximation. Thus, in what follows we will consider approximations of *irrational* numbers α only.

The best rational approximations to a real number α are its convergents p_n/q_n. By formula (14) (page 41) the distance from p_n/q_n to α is estimated by

(4) $$|q_n\alpha - p_n| < 1/q_n$$

whatever the approximated number α is. Thus, *every* successive convergent p_{n+1}/q_{n+1}, etc., is closer to α than the previous one, and all satisfy inequality (4) in which an estimate of the right-hand side is expressed by the "unit" $1/q_n$ of the convergent p_n/q_n which approximates the number α. However, it is not indispensable to have *all* successive approximations p_n/q_n satisfy the inequality (4) in order to approximate α as closely as we please. It is possible to skip some of the successive convergents, but we must always have at our disposal *infinitely many* convergents from which to choose. Now we may ask whether there can be some estimate smaller than $1/q_n$ on the right-hand side of (4). More precisely, the question is: What is the smallest possible constant λ that will assure that every real number α has *infinitely many* rational approximations p/q satisfying the inequality

(5) $$|q\alpha - p| < \lambda/q$$

In 1891 A. Hurwitz proved that $\lambda = 1/\sqrt{5}$, and it cannot be replaced by any smaller constant. In 1903 E. Borel strengthened this theorem in the following respect: Suppose, for fixed α, we picked up one of its convergents p_n/q_n and checked whether it satisfied (5) with $\lambda = 1/\sqrt{5}$. If it does not, we try the next one, p_{n+1}/q_{n+1}; and if this does not either, we try the next one, p_{n+2}/q_{n+2}. Hurwitz' theorem does not tell us how long we have to try until we get a convergent that satisfies (5). It only assures us that there are many to choose from.

Hurwitz-Borel Theorem. *If* $\lambda = 1/\sqrt{5}$, *then for every real number* α *at least one of its three consecutive convergents* $p_n/q_n, p_{n+1}/q_{n+1}, p_{n+2}/q_{n+2}$, *satisfy the inequality*

$$(5) \qquad |q\alpha - p| < \lambda/q$$

If $\lambda < 1/\sqrt{5}$, *there exist such real numbers* α *for which only a finite number of rationals* p/q *can satisfy the inequality* (5).

Proof of the first statement is based on the formula (11) (page 37) written as

$$q_{m+1} |q_m \alpha - p_m| + q_m |q_{m+1} \alpha - p_{m+1}| = 1$$

By denoting

$$(i) \qquad \varphi_m = q_m |q_m \alpha - p_m|$$

that formula is

$$\frac{q_{m+1}}{q_m} \varphi_m + \frac{q_m}{q_{m+1}} \varphi_{m+1} = 1$$

Put $m = n + 1$, and solve the equation with respect to q_{n+2}/q_{n+1}. Then put $m = n$, and solve the equation with respect to q_n/q_{n+1}. We get, after calculation,

$$\frac{q_{n+2}}{q_{n+1}} = \frac{1}{2\varphi_{n+1}} \left(1 + \sqrt{1 - 4\varphi_{n+1}\varphi_{n+2}} \right)$$

and

$$\frac{q_n}{q_{n+1}} = \frac{1}{2\varphi_{n+1}} \left(1 - \sqrt{1 - 4\varphi_n \varphi_{n+1}} \right)$$

In the first solution the sign of the radical is positive, because $q_{n+2}/q_{n+1} > 1$. In the second solution the sign is negative, because $q_n/q_{n+1} < 1$. Substitute this into formula (2) (page 31) written as

$$(q_{n+2}/q_{n+1}) - (q_n/q_{n+1}) = a_{n+2}$$

to get the formula which does the proof:

$$(ii) \qquad \frac{1}{2\varphi_{n+1}} \left(\sqrt{1 - 4\varphi_n\varphi_{n+1}} + \sqrt{1 - 4\varphi_{n+1}\varphi_{n+2}} \right) = a_{n+2}$$

In fact, now let φ_m be the *smallest* of the three numbers φ_n, φ_{n+1}, φ_{n+2}. Substituting φ_m in (ii) in place of all the φ's increases the left-hand expression. On the other hand, $a_{n+2} \geq 1$. Therefore,

$$\sqrt{1 - 4\varphi_m^2}/\varphi_m > 1$$

whence $\varphi_m < 1/\sqrt{5}$. By notation (i) this is exactly what the first part of the theorem says.[3]

As to the second part, we shall prove that for the "golden" number $\gamma = \frac{1}{2}(\sqrt{5} - 1)$ only a *finite* number of rationals p/q can satisfy inequality (5) if $\lambda < 1/\sqrt{5}$.

The idea of the proof is as follows: Suppose that for the number γ there is $\lambda < 1/\sqrt{5}$ *and* inequality (5) can be satisfied by *infinitely many* rationals p/q. Since now $\lambda < 1/\sqrt{5} < 1/2$, inequality (5) shows that the numbers p/q satisfy condition (3). Thus, they must be convergents to γ. On the other hand, we will prove that those convergents to γ satisfy the inequality

(iii)
$$|q_n\gamma - p_n| > \frac{1}{q_n[\sqrt{5} + (1/q_n^2)]}$$

This, together with the inequality (5), would imply that for *infinitely many* convergents

$$0 < \frac{1}{\lambda} - \sqrt{5} < \frac{1}{q_n^2}$$

But this is impossible, because on the right-hand side the greatest lower bound of all $1/q_n^2$ is 0. Thus, it could not be greater than the supposedly positive fixed number $1/\lambda - \sqrt{5}$.

Finally, here is the proof of inequality (iii). First, we notice that in the continued fraction expansion of the "golden" number γ all the remainders ρ_n are equal to $1/\gamma$. Hence by formula (10), page 37,

$$\gamma = \frac{p_n + p_{n-1}\gamma}{q_n + q_{n-1}\gamma}$$

Thus,

(iv)
$$|q_n\gamma - p_n| = \frac{1}{q_n[(1/\gamma) + (q_{n-1}/q_n)]}$$

Second, we notice that q_{n-1}/q_n is the nth convergent p_n/q_n to γ. In fact, since in the continued fraction all the digits $a_n = 1$, for γ

$$p_n = p_{n-1} + p_{n-2}, \quad q_n = q_{n-1} + q_{n-2}$$

and since

$$p_0 = 0, \quad q_0 = 1, \quad p_1 = 1, \quad q_1 = 1$$

we check by induction that $p_n = q_{n-1}$.

Therefore, inequality (14), page 41, gives

$$\left| \gamma - \frac{q_{n-1}}{q_n} \right| < \frac{1}{q_n^2}$$

whence

$$\gamma - \frac{q_{n-1}}{q_n} > -\frac{1}{q_n^2}$$

Thus,

$$\frac{q_{n-1}}{q_n} < \gamma + \frac{1}{q_n^2}$$

Add $1/\gamma$ to both sides and notice, finally, that $\gamma + (1/\gamma) = \sqrt{5}$, and that $\gamma < 1/\gamma$, to get

$$\gamma + \frac{q_{n-1}}{q_n} < \sqrt{5} + \frac{1}{q_n^2}$$

Substitute this into (iv) to prove the announced inequality (iii). This completes the entire proof.

The Hurwitz-Borel theorem guarantees to *every* real number α the "right" to have infinitely many rational approximations p/q from which to choose in order to be approximated with an error $|\alpha - (p/q)|$ not exceeding $1/\sqrt{5}q^2$. But, it does not guarantee to *any* real number a closer approximation. Moreover, it says that if this law of approximation is to be *universal* for all real numbers, it cannot be improved by taking instead of $1/\sqrt{5}$ any smaller constant λ. If $\lambda < 1/\sqrt{5}$, there are such numbers α for which equality (5) has only a finite number of rational solutions p/q, so we do not have an unlimited choice. Such a number has been exhibited in the proof of the theorem: The "golden" number γ, which satisfies the equation

$$\gamma^2 - \gamma + 1 = 0$$

In a way, we could say that the "golden" number is *worst* approximable by rationals. That "bad" property is shared by the "golden" number with any other number that has successive digits 1 from some place in its continued fraction expansion. This can be seen if we analyze the second part of the proof, where essentially only that property was exploited. Thus, the class of the worst approximable real numbers consists of all numbers equivalent with the "golden" number. See page 45.

Suppose we exclude from the real numbers all those "bad" numbers equivalent to the "golden" number. What would be the law of approximation for the remaining numbers? In 1879 A. Markoff proved that instead of $\lambda = 1/\sqrt{5}$, we can take a smaller number $\lambda_1 = 1/\sqrt{8}$, and then the "bad" numbers are all those equivalent to a number γ_1, which satisfies the equation

$$\gamma_1^2 + 2\gamma_1 - 1 = 0$$

for instance, we can take $\gamma_2 = \sqrt{2} - 1$. All those numbers have the period of digits $(2, 1, 1)$ starting from some place in their continued fraction expansions. Furthermore, if we proceed this way and exclude those second worst numbers, the remaining numbers can be approximated with $\lambda_2 = 5/\sqrt{221}$, and the "bad" numbers now are equivalent to the number γ_2, which satisfies the equation

$$13\gamma_2^2 + 29\gamma_2 - 13 = 0$$

and so on. In this way one gets an infinite, decreasing sequence of constants λ_k,

$$1/\sqrt{5}, \quad 1/\sqrt{8}, \quad 5/\sqrt{221}, \quad 13/\sqrt{1517}, \ldots$$

and it can be proved[4] that the sequence of these numbers has the greatest lower bound $1/3$. However, after having expelled all these "bad" numbers there still remain almost all reals. See page 84. Notice that all these "bad" numbers are algebraic of degree 2.

3. Approximation of Algebraic Numbers

By the Hurwitz-Borel theorem every real number α can be approximated by infinitely many rationals p/q satisfying the inequality

$$|\alpha - (p/q)| < 1/\sqrt{5}q^2,$$

but some numbers cannot be approximated more accurately.

It does not matter here whether we use the distance $|\alpha - (p/q)|$ or $|q\alpha - p|$. We take the first one for traditional reasons, which will be clear from what follows.

The accuracy of the approximation can be measured by any function $\lambda(q)$ of a natural variable, instead of $1/\sqrt{5}q^2$. In this discussion we shall confine ourselves to the following definition. We say that *a number* α *can be approximated with accuracy of degree m if the inequality*

(6) $$|\alpha - (p/q)| < 1/q^m$$

has infinitely many rational solutions p/q.

Any number that can be approximated with accuracy of degree m can also be approximated with accuracy of any degree less than m. By the Universal Law, every real number can be approximated with accuracy of degree 2, because $1/\sqrt{5} < 1$. But the "golden" number and, more generally, all the "bad" Markoff numbers, mentioned at the end of Section 2, cannot be approximated with accuracy of degree greater than 2. Which other numbers are also badly approximable? In 1851 J. Liouville proved that no algebraic number of degree n can be approximated with accuracy of degree higher than $(n + 1)$.

Liouville's Theorem on Algebraic Numbers. *If* α *is an algebraic number of degree n it must be that*

(7) $$|\alpha - (p/q)| \geq 1/q^{n+1}$$

for all rationals p/q, except possibly for a finite number of them.

Proof. Let us examine those rationals p/q for which inequality (7) *cannot* hold. The proof that there can be at the most a finite number of rationals p/q is based on the following two arguments.

The first argument is that, if inequality (7) does *not* hold, there must be

(i) $$|p/q| < |\alpha| + 1$$

In fact, since

$$|p/q| - |\alpha| \leq |\alpha - (p/q)|$$

and $q \geq 1$, the inequality

$$|\alpha - (p/q)| < 1/q^{n+1}$$

implies (i).

The second argument is to prove that if the inequality (7) does not hold, the denominators $q \geq 1$ of the rationals p/q must be bounded by a fixed number b; i.e., that

$$1 \leq q < b$$

Then, by (i) it will follow that the numerators p must also be bounded, viz.

$$|p| < b(|\alpha| + 1)$$

and since there is only a finite number of such rationals p/q, the theorem will be proved.

The proof of the second argument runs as follows. Since α is an algebraic number of degree $n > 1$, there exists a polynomial.

$$P_n(x) = A_n x^n + A_{n-1} x^{n+1} + \ldots + A_1 x + A_0$$

with *integer* coefficients

$$A_n \neq 0, \quad A_{n-1}, \ldots, A_1, A_0$$

such that $P_n(\alpha) = 0$ (see page 9), and there is no such polynomial of degree less than n. Hence, it follows that α must be irrational; otherwise, it would nullify a polynomial of first degree. We shall show that the polynomial $P_n(x)$ has no rational roots. In fact, if $x = p/q$, then, since $P_n(\alpha) = 0$, we have

$$P_n\left(\frac{p}{q}\right) = P_n\left(\frac{p}{q}\right) - P_n(\alpha)$$

$$= A_n\left(\left(\frac{p}{q}\right)^n - \alpha^n\right) + \ldots + A_2\left(\left(\frac{p}{q}\right)^2 - \alpha^2\right) + A_1\left(\frac{p}{q} - \alpha\right),$$

whence

(ii) $\left|P_n\left(\frac{p}{q}\right)\right| = \left|\alpha - \frac{p}{q}\right| \cdot \left|A_n\left(\alpha^{n-1} + \frac{p}{q}\alpha^{n-2} + \ldots + \left(\frac{p}{q}\right)^{n-1}\right)\right.$

$$\left. + \ldots + A_2\left(\alpha + \frac{p}{q}\right) + A_1\right|.$$

Should $P_n(p/q) = 0$, then, since the irrational $\alpha \neq p/q$, the second factor on the right-hand side would vanish. But, that factor is a polynomial in α degree of $(n - 1)$ with *rational* coefficients, and its vanishing contradicts the assumption that α does not nullify any such polynomial with degree less than n. Thus, $P_n(p/q) \neq 0$. This implies that for *any* rational p/q

(iii) $$|P_n(p/q)| = \frac{1}{q^n}|A_n p^n + \ldots + A_0 q^n| \geq 1/q^n$$

because the integer

$$|A_n p^n + \ldots + A_0 q^n| \geq 1$$

Now, consider those p/q for which inequality (7) does *not* hold. These p/q must satisfy (i). Also, since

$$|p/q| < |\alpha| + 1$$

because

$$|\alpha| < |\alpha| + 1$$

we have by (iii) and (ii) that for those p/q there must be

$$\frac{1}{q^n} \leq \left|\alpha - \frac{p}{q}\right| \cdot \{|A_n| \cdot \left(|\alpha|^{n-1} + \left|\frac{p}{q}\right| \cdot |\alpha|^{n-2} + \ldots + \left|\frac{p}{q}\right|^{n-1}\right) + \ldots$$

$$+ |A_2|\left(|\alpha| + \left|\frac{p}{q}\right|\right) + |A_1|\}$$

$$< \left|\alpha - \frac{p}{q}\right| \cdot \{|A_n|\, n(|\alpha| + 1)^{n-1} + \ldots + |A_2| \cdot 2(|\alpha| + 1) + |A_1|\}$$

Denote the number in braces, fixed and independent of p/q, by b. Then, if (7) does *not* hold; i.e., if

$$|\alpha - (p/q)| < 1/q^{n+1}$$

then

$$1/q^n < |\alpha - (p/q)|\, b$$

Hence, it follows that $q < b$. This completes the entire proof.

The theorem indicates that algebraic numbers cannot be approximated with accuracy of *any* given degree $m > 2$. Are there, among real numbers, those that might be better approximated? If they exist, they must be non-algebraic; i.e., transcendental. Liouville exhibited infinitely many such numbers.

A real number α is called a Liouville's number if it can be approximated with accuracy of any given degree $m > 2$.

Theorem on Liouville's Numbers. *For any given exponent $m > 2$ there always exist (irrational) numbers α such that the inequality*

$$(8) \qquad\qquad |\alpha - (p/q)| < 1/q^m$$

has infinitely many rational solutions p/q.

Proof. Given m, the number α can be constructed by its continued fraction expansion in the following way. Starting with an arbitrary digit a_0, take the successive digits such that

$$a_{k+1} > q_k^{m-2}$$

Then, by formulae (12) and (2), (Sec. 2, Ch. II) there will be

$$\left| \alpha - \frac{p_k}{q_k} \right| < \frac{1}{q_k q_{k+1}} = \frac{1}{q_k(q_k a_{k+1} + q_{k-1})} < \frac{1}{q_k^2 a_{k+1}} < \frac{1}{q_k^m}$$

for *all* convergents p_k/q_k to α. Thus, for infinitely many rationals p/q, as desired.

For rational α the theorem is trivially true, because the last convergent p_l/q_l to α and infinitely many rationals rp_l/rp_l make the left-hand side in (6) equal to zero.

The theorem can be cheaply but noticeably strengthened by taking in (6) any given—however small—function $\lambda(q)$ of the natural variable q instead of $1/q^m$. The idea of the proof need not be changed. We simply take

$$a_{k+1} > \frac{1}{q_k^2 \lambda(q_k)}$$

Moreover, it can be perceived that if the function $\lambda(q)$, which estimates the error of the approximation, is small, the digits a_k should be large. Furthermore, the smaller the digits a_k, the harder it is to approximate the number α. That is why the "golden" number with all its digits as small as possible; i.e., equal to 1, is the hardest to approximate.

No Liouville's number can be algebraic. They are all transcendental. In fact, inequality (8) for $m = n + 1$ contradicts (7).

Liouville's numbers were historically the first transcendental numbers to be exhibited. They are by no means the only transcendental numbers. More than 20 years after Liouville's work G. Cantor proved, in an entirely different way, that most real numbers are transcendental Algebraic numbers are a paltry part of the reals. See page 86.

Although there are so many transcendental numbers, it is difficult to prove that some specific number is transcendental. In 1873 Ch. Hermite proved that the number e, the base for natural logarithm, is transcendental. On page 28 we only proved that e is irrational. Following Hermite's work, F. Lindemann proved in 1882 that π is transcendental. The fact that π cannot satisfy any algebraic equation with rational coefficients implies that it is impossible to construct, using ruler and compass only, a segment of the length π, a problem called quadrature of the circle, which has resisted solution for more than 2000 years.[5] In 1934 A. O. Gelfond and T. Schneider proved independently that, if α and β are algebraic numbers with $0 \neq \alpha \neq 1$ and β is irrational, then α^β is transcendental, giving the solution to the seventh of the famous 23 problems that D. Hilbert announced in 1900 as a challenge for twentieth-century mathematics.[6] The number represented by the decimal expansion 1.2345 . . . , and the number represented by the continued fraction expansion 1:2345 . . . , have also been proved transcendental.[7]

Not very much is known about transcendental numbers. We do not know whether $e + \pi$, $e - \pi$, or $e\pi$ are transcendental. We even do not know whether they are irrational. The very hard surface of these problems has only been scratched.

Problems concerning algebraic numbers are not easy, either. By Liouville's Theorem algebraic numbers (of degree n) cannot be approximated with accuracy of degree $m > n$. Can they be approximated with accuracy of degree less than n? By the Universal Law of Approximation there must be $m \geq 2$. The suspicion that the bound for m can be lowered to 2 for *all* algebraic numbers, regardless of their degree, was not resolved for more than 100 years. In 1909 A. Thue lowered the bound to $(n/2) + 1$. In 1921 C. L. Siegel lowered $(n/2) + 1$ to $2\sqrt{n}$. In 1947 F. J. Dyson and A. O. Gelfond independently lowered $2\sqrt{n}$ to $\sqrt{2n}$. Finally, in 1955 K. F. Roth[8] achieved the bound 2. That is, he proved that no (irrational) algebraic number can be approximated with degree of accuracy $m > 2$. Thus, we may say that with respect to their ability to be approximated by rationals, all algebraic numbers, regardless of their degree greater than 2, are no better than the algebraic numbers of degree 2.

The (irrational) algebraic numbers are those which can be defined by finite sets of integers (see page 9). Thus, Roth's theorem indicates that an (irrational) number that can be defined by means of a finite set of integers cannot be approximated (by rationals) with degree of accuracy higher than 2.

By the Theorem on Periodic Continued Fractions, page 42, all quadratic (irrational) algebraic numbers have periodic continued fractions. Thus, the digits in the continued fractions of these numbers are *bounded*. It is not known whether the digits in a continued fraction expansion of any algebraic number of degree higher than 2 are also bounded. It follows from Roth's result that the digits a_n of any algebraic number must satisfy the condition that however small the positive number ε, there must be

$$a_n < e^{(1+\varepsilon)^n}$$

but not much more is known. Thus, for example, it is not known whether the digits in the continued fraction expansion of $\sqrt[3]{2}$ are bounded, not to mention more specific information about the rule for those digits. It has been checked[9] by electronic computer that among the 750 first digits of the continued fraction expansion of $\sqrt[3]{2}$ the largest was $a_{321} = 22054$.

4. Diophantine Approximations

We shall now discuss from another point of view the approximations of real numbers by rationals to explore the distribution of irrational numbers.

By Hurwitz-Borel theorem (page 61), it follows that every real number α can be approximated by a rational p/q, with natural denominator q, in such a way that

(1) $$|q\alpha - p| < 1/q$$

This fact can also be expressed as follows: Given any real number α, there always exist integer solutions $q \geq 1$ and p of inequality (1). Problems concerning integer solutions of inequalities are called Diophantine Approximations. We shall give only few samples of those problems here.

The name refers to Diophantus of Alexandria, mathematician of the second century A.D., who studied integer solutions of equations.

The existence of integer solutions for inequality (1) has been proved, so far, by use of continued fraction expansion of the number α. However, this same fact, and others, can be proved by another argument based on the "box principle" (see page 5). We shall prove the following theorem, due to Dirichlet.

Given any real number α, and any natural number t, there always exist infinitely many integer solutions q, p of the inequality

$$(2) \qquad |q\alpha - p| < 1/t$$

The *proof* is Dirichlet's. Consider the interval $[0, 1)$ including 0 but not 1. Divide the interval into t equal subintervals of the length $1/t$, closed at left and open at right. Given α, consider the sequence $n\alpha$ with natural n running over $1, 2, \ldots, t, t + 1$. If, as before, $[n\alpha]$ denotes the greatest integer not exceeding $n\alpha$; i.e., such that

$$[n\alpha] \leq n\alpha < [n\alpha] + 1$$

then each of the $(t + 1)$ numbers

$$(3) \qquad \{n\alpha\} = n\alpha - [n\alpha]$$

is the *fractional part* of $n\alpha$. Thus,

$$0 \leq \{n\alpha\} < 1$$

i.e., all the fractions must be in the interval $[0, 1)$. However, there are only t subintervals and $t + 1$ fractions $\{n\alpha\}$. By the "box principle" at least two fractional parts $\{n\alpha\}$ for different n's, say $n_2 > n_1$, must fall into the same subinterval of the length $1/t$; i.e.,

$$|\{n_2\alpha\} - \{n_1\alpha\}| < 1/t$$

Take

$$q = n_2 - n_1 \quad \text{and} \quad p = [n_2\alpha] - [n_1\alpha]$$

to get the integers q and p, which satisfy the inequality (2). Moreover, since

$$0 < n_2 - n_1 \leq t$$

there must be $1 \leq q \leq t$; i.e., q cannot be too large. On the other hand, we also can find the natural number q as large as we want by letting the

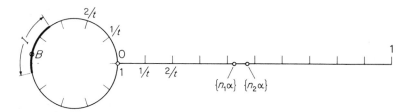

Figure 5

natural n run not only to $t + 1$ but also arbitrarily long. Thus, there are infinitely many q's with p's corresponding to each of them.

The subintervals taken are closed at one end and open at the other in order to avoid the rather trivial situation when the number α is rational and the fractions $\{n_2\alpha\}$ and $\{n_1\alpha\}$ coincide with the ends of the intervals.

Dirichlet's argument, simple as it is, reveals more. Let us analyze inequality (2) written as

$$-1/t < p - q\alpha < 1/t.$$

Hence, from

$$0 \le q\alpha - [q\alpha] < 1$$

it follows, by addition, that

$$-1/t < p - [q\alpha] < 1 + 1/t$$

and, since $t \ge 1$ and both p and $[q\alpha]$ are integers, there must be

$$0 \le p - [q\alpha] \le 1$$

which implies that p is either $[q\alpha]$ or $[q\alpha] + 1$. Thus, $q\alpha - p$ is either $\{q\alpha\}$ or $\{q\alpha\} - 1$. Therefore, inequality (2) means that the fractional part $\{q\alpha\}$ satisfies either the inequality

$$\{q\alpha\} < 1/t \quad \text{or} \quad 1 - \{q\alpha\} < 1/t$$

In these terms, Dirichlet's theorem states that, given any real number α, one can find such a natural number q that the fractional part $\{q\alpha\}$ can be at a distance less than $1/t$ from either 0 or 1, however small we choose $1/t$.

This situation can be made more suggestive by the following geometrical interpretation, Figure 5. Roll up the interval $[0, 1)$ into a circle with the *perimeter* 1. Then, the ends of that interval coincide at one point, which we shall call O. Starting from O, divide the circle into t equal arcs of length $1/t$. Dirichlet's theorem says that, given any real number α, there is always a natural q such that the fractional part $\{q\alpha\}$ falls within a circular distance $1/t$ from point O, however small $1/t$ is.

Next we may ask if this is true if we take, instead of the point O, any other point B on the circle. If the number α is rational it is not so. In fact, if $\alpha = l/m$ with natural m, there are only m different fractional parts $\{q\alpha\}$ for any natural q—namely, $0/m, 1/m, 2/m, \ldots, (m-1)/m$, which mark on the circle m equidistant points, starting at O. If the point B is given, its distance from the nearest of those points is fixed and cannot be made smaller than any prescribed $1/t$.

However, if α is *irrational*, then Dirichlet's theorem can be generalized by taking any point B instead of O. Let us state that fact in arithmetical terms. The point B on the circle represents the fractional part $\{\beta\}$ of the given number β. Thus, we claim that for any given irrational α, the distance $|\{q\alpha\} - \{\beta\}|$ can be made as small as we please. Or, if we denote $[q\alpha] - [\beta]$ by p, we shall prove the following theorem due to Kronecker.

Given any irrational number α, any real number β, and any natural number t, there exist infinitely many integers $q \geq 1$ and p, which satisfy the inequality

$$(4) \qquad\qquad |q\alpha - p - \beta| < 1/t$$

Proof. Divide the circle into t equal arcs, starting from the point O. By Dirichlet's theorem, there is a natural q_0 such that $\{q_0\alpha\}$ falls within the interval $(0, 1/t)$. Take the sequence of points corresponding to the numbers $k\{q_0\alpha\}$ for k over $1, 2, \ldots, [1/\{q_0\alpha\}]$. They all are of the form $\{l\alpha\}$ with some natural l, since α is irrational. Also, each of the subintervals of length $1/t$ on the circle contains at least one of these points. Thus, there must be at least one point at a distance smaller than $1/t$ from point $\{\beta\}$. By continuing the sequence $k\{q_0\alpha\}$ infinitely, we get infinitely many and arbitrarily large integer numbers q and p that satisfy inequality (4).

Comparing this theorem with the Hurwitz-Borel theorem, we may ask what is the smallest possible constant μ such that, for *any* irrational number α and *any* real number β, the inequality

$$|q\alpha - p - \beta| < \mu/q$$

has infinitely many integer solutions q, p. H. Minkowski proved[10] that $\mu = 1/4$.

Kronecker's theorem means that, if the number α is irrational, then in every interval on the circle, however small, there can be found points corresponding to $\{n\alpha\}$ with some natural n. One also says that the set of all fractional parts $\{n\alpha\}$, $n = 1, 2, \ldots$ is, for every irrational α, *everywhere dense* in the interval $(0, 1)$. We shall now prove more. The fractional parts $\{n\alpha\}$, $n = 1, 2, \ldots$, of every irrational α are *uniformly distributed* in the interval $(0, 1)$. More precisely, we shall prove the following

Theorem on Uniform Distribution. *Let I be any interval contained in $[0, 1]$. Given any irrational α, let $v_n(I)$ for $n = 1, 2, \ldots$, denote the number of those fractional parts $\{i\alpha\}$, for $i = 1, 2, \ldots, n$, that fall into the interval I. Then, for every irrational α, the frequency $(1/n)v_n(I)$ tends to the length of the interval I as n tends to infinity.*

Here is an outline of the proof. First, notice that we can confine ourselves to intervals with their left ends at O. In fact, every other interval is a difference of two such intervals, and similarly, the frequency is equal to the difference of the corresponding frequencies.

Thus, the essential point consists in examining the frequency $(1/n)v_n(I)$ for the interval $I = (0, \lambda)$ with $0 \le \lambda \le 1$. Basically, instead of the given irrational α, we shall take its convergents and examine the corresponding frequency $(1/n)v'_n$ for these convergents. Since the convergents approximate the given α as closely as we please, we shall draw conclusions from the behavior of $(1/n)v'_n$ about the behavior of $(1/n)v_n(I)$.

Let p_k/q_k be the kth convergent of α, and let

$$A'_j = \{jp_k/q_k\}$$

for fixed k. We want to estimate how many times the points A'_j (for

$j = 1, 2, \ldots, n$) fall into the interval $I = (0, \lambda)$. To this end, take a subinterval I_k contained in I with ends at m/q_k and $\lambda - (m/q_k)$, where m is a natural number to be disposed of later. Besides I_k, consider a still smaller interval I_k' with the ends at m/q_k and $(l - m)/q_k$, where $l = [\lambda q_k]$.

Now, we shall estimate the number $v_n'(I_k')$, incidating how many times the points A_j' (for $j = 1, 2, \ldots, n$) fall into the interval I_k'. Since we intend to go with n to infinity, we may start with $n \geq q_k$.

If $n = q_k$, then the numbers

$$A_j' = \{jp_k/q_k\}$$

are of the form i/q_k with $i = 0, 1, 2, \ldots, q_k - 1$ arranged in some order. They are all different, because p_k/q_k is in its lowest terms. Those of the numbers i/q_k fall into the interval

$$I_k' = [m/q_k, (l - m)/q_k]$$

for which $m \leq i \leq l - m$. Hence, $l - 2m + 1$ of the points A_j' fall into the interval I_k'.

If $n > q_k$, then the numbers A_j', with

$$j = 1, 2, \ldots, (q_k - 1), \quad q_k, \ldots, n$$

are of the same form as before, but there will be only q_k of them different; i.e., some points A_j' will repeat. However, we shall count them as many times as they actually occur. We do so because the numbers $A_j = \{j\alpha\}$, to which we will pass later, will *not* repeat, since they are irrational. Thus, the numbers A_j', with $j = 1, 2, \ldots, n$, fall into the interval at least $[n/q_k]$ times more often than before; i.e., when j was running over $1, 2, \ldots, q_k$. Hence, we get for the sought number

$$v_n'(I_k') = \left[\frac{n}{q_k}\right](l - 2m + 1)$$

Since

$$\left[\frac{n}{q_k}\right] > \frac{n}{q_k} - 1 \quad \text{and} \quad l + 1 > \lambda q_k$$

we have

$$\frac{1}{n}v_n'(I_k') > \frac{1}{n}\left(\frac{n}{q_k} - 1\right)(\lambda q_k - 2m) > \lambda - \frac{2m}{q_k} - \frac{\lambda q_k}{n}$$

The last expression can be made as close to the length λ of interval I as we please. In fact, take any $\varepsilon > 0$. For fixed k, make

$$m < \frac{\varepsilon}{2}\lambda q_k \quad \text{and} \quad n > \frac{q_k}{\varepsilon}$$

Thus, we may say that with fixed k, for any $\varepsilon > 0$, however small, the frequency of numbers

$$A'_j = \{jp_k/q_k\}$$

$j = 1, 2, \ldots, n$, falling into the interval I'_k has the estimate

$$\frac{1}{n}\nu'_n(I'_k) \geq \lambda(1 - 2\varepsilon)$$

for sufficiently large n.

We pass now to the numbers

$$A_j = \{j\alpha\}$$

$j = 1, 2, \ldots, n$. The convergents p_k/q_k approximate the irrational number α with accuracy

$$\left|\alpha - \frac{p_k}{q_k}\right| < \frac{1}{q_k q_{k+1}}$$

as in formula (12), page 37. Hence,

$$\left|j\alpha - \frac{jp_k}{q_k}\right| < \frac{j}{q_k q_{k+1}} \leq \frac{n}{q_k q_{k+1}}$$

and since q_k's increase with k, we can make

$$\frac{n}{q_k q_{k+1}} < \varepsilon\lambda/2$$

for any n considered. From the definition of the interval I_k it can be checked that if

$$|j\alpha - jp_k/q_k| < \varepsilon\lambda/2$$

and if $\{jp_k/q_k\}$ falls into the interval I_k, then $\{j\alpha\}$ falls into the slightly larger interval I.

Let us recapitulate. Given any $\varepsilon > 0$, however small, the sought frequency $(1/n)\nu_n(I)$ has for

$$q_k/\varepsilon < n < \tfrac{1}{2}\varepsilon\lambda q_k q_{k+1}$$

the estimate

$$(1/n)\nu_n(I) > \lambda(1 - 2\varepsilon)$$

Thus, if k, and consequently n, is sufficiently large, the frequency of the numbers $\{j\alpha\}$, $j = 1, 2, \ldots, n$, falling into the interval $I = (0, \lambda)$ satisfies the inequality

$$(1/n)v_n(I) > \lambda - 2\varepsilon$$

To complete the proof, consider the interval J, complementary to I in the whole interval $(0, 1)$. The length of J is $\mu = 1 - \lambda$. By the same argument as before, we can say that for the frequency of the numbers $\{j\alpha\}, j = 1, 2, \ldots, n$, falling into the interval J, we have with large n

$$(1/n)v_n(J) > \mu - 2\varepsilon$$

However,

$$(1/n)v_n(I) + (1/n)v_n(J) = 1$$

because the number $\{j\alpha\}$ must fall either to I or to J. Hence,

$$(1/n)v_n(I) = 1 - (1/n)v_n(J) < 1 - \mu + 2\varepsilon = \lambda + 2\varepsilon$$

We conclude that, for any given $\varepsilon > 0$, however small, we can find sufficiently large n such that

$$\lambda - 2\varepsilon < (1/n)v_n(I) < \lambda + 2\varepsilon$$

which means that the frequency $(1/n)v_n(I)$ tends to the length λ of the interval I, as stated in the theorem.

The Theorem on Uniform Distribution can be illustrated, to a certain extent, by a roulette game. If we stake many times on the same ticket, our chances of winning or losing are roughly the same as if we stake once at many various tickets.

There are many other problems in Diophantine Approximations. For instance, one can generalize all the theorems above to more than one dimension; i.e., when one asks for approximation of not one real number α but of several real numbers $\alpha_1, \alpha_2, \ldots, \alpha_n$ by rationals. Thus, the Dirichlet's theorem can be immediately extended by the same "box principle" as follows. Given n real numbers $\alpha_1, \alpha_2, \ldots, \alpha_n$ and a natural number t, the inequality

$$|q_1\alpha_1 + q_2\alpha_2 + \ldots + q_n\alpha_n - p| < 1/t^n$$

always has integer solutions $q_1, q_2, \ldots, q_n, p$ such that not all the q's are simultaneously zero; moreover, one can always have

$$|q_i| < 1/t$$

$i = 1, 2, \ldots, n$. To prove this divide the interval $[0, 1)$ into t^n equal parts and apply the "box principle." Another generalization says that the system of simultaneous inequalities

$$|q\alpha_1 - p_1| < 1/t, \quad \ldots, \quad |q\alpha_n - p_n| < 1/t$$

always has integer solutions $q, p_1, p_2, \ldots, p_n$; moreover, one can always have

$$1 \leq q \leq t^n$$

The proof consists in applying the "box principle" to an n-dimensional cube with side 1.

Generalizations of Kronecker's theorem require different methods, as do the generalizations of the Theorem of Uniform Distribution. Geometrical arguments are often used, and for this reason the theory is also called Geometry of Numbers.[11]

REFERENCES

(1) F. Klein, *Elementary Mathematics from an Advanced Point of View*. (New York: Dover Publications, Inc., 1932) pp. 44.

(2) See L. R. Ford, Fractions, *Amer. Math. Monthly*, Vol. 45, 1938, pp. 586; also, J. Züllig, *Geometrische Deutung unendlicher Kettenbrüche und ihre Approximation durch rationale Zahlen* (Zurich: Orell Fussli, 1928).

(3) The idea for this proof has been taken from the paper: M. Fujiwara, Remarks on the Theory of Approximation of Irrational Numbers by Rational Numbers, *Japanese Journal of Mathematics*, Vol. 1, 1923, pp. 15–16.

(4) See J. W. C. Cassels, *An Introduction to Diophantine Approximation*. (New York: Cambridge University Press, 1957) Chapter II.

(5) For proofs of transcendance of ρ and π, see G. H. Hardy and E. M. Wright, *An Introduction to the Theory of Numbers*, 3rd ed. (Oxford, The Clarendon Press, 1956) pp. 170–176; or I. Niven, *Irrational Numbers*, Carus Monographs. (New York: John Wiley & Sons, Inc., 1956) Chapter 2.

(6) For proof, see I. Niven, *ibid*, Chapter 10.

(7) See C. L. Siegel, *Transcendental Numbers*. (Princeton, N.J.: Princeton University Press, 1949).

(8) The proof can be found in Cassels, *op. cit.*, Chapter VI.

(9) R. D. Richtmyer, Marjorie Devaney, and N. Metropolis, Continued fraction expansion of algebraic numbers, *Numerische Mathematik*, **4**, (1962), pp. 68–84.

(10) For proof, see Hardy and Wright, *op. cit.*, pp. 339–403; or Cassels, *op. cit.* pp. 46–51; or I. Niven, Minkowski's Theorem on Nonhomogeneous Approximation, *Proceedings of the Amer. Math. Soc.*, Vol. 12, No. 6, 1961, pp. 992–993.

(11) See Hardy and Wright, *op. cit.*, Chapter XXIII and XXIV.

IV

Cardinality and Measure of Sets of Real Numbers

In this chapter we shall examine and answer such questions as: "How many rational, algebraic, or transcendental numbers are there in a given set of real numbers?" One way of doing this uses the cardinality of a set; another uses the measure of a set.

I. Cardinality

The concept of cardinality of a set, introduced in the second half of the nineteenth century by G. Cantor, expresses the idea of the number of elements contained in a given set. It is defined in the following way.

We first introduce a relation, between two sets, of being *equinumerous*. Two sets are called equinumerous if it is possible to establish a one-to-one correspondence between the elements of the sets. It follows that this relation is: 1° reflexive; i.e., every set is equinumerous with itself; 2° symmetric; i.e., if the set $\mathscr{U}$ is equinumerous with $\mathscr{V}$, so is $\mathscr{V}$ with $\mathscr{U}$;

3° transitive; i.e., if $\mathscr{U}$ is equinumerous with $\mathscr{V}$, and $\mathscr{V}$ is equinumerous with the set $\mathscr{W}$, then $\mathscr{U}$ is equinumerous with $\mathscr{W}$.

Then, the *cardinality* of a given set is defined as the *set* of all sets equinumerous with the given set. For example, the two sets $\{a, b, c\}$ and $\{x, y, z\}$, whatever the letters mean, are equinumerous; that is, there is a one-to-one correspondence between elements: the element a corresponds to the element x; also, b corresponds to y, and c to z. Thus, the cardinality of the set $\{a, b, c\}$ is the set of all sets equinumerous with the set $\{a, b, c\}$. Denoting this cardinality by the symbol 3 ("three") we could consider that cardinality as a natural number.

Cantor described[1] cardinality as "the general concept which, by means of our active faculty of thought, arises from the aggregate $\mathscr{M}$ when we make abstraction of the nature of its various elements m and of the order in which they are given." To emphasize "this double act of abstraction"—viz. of the "nature" and of the "order"—Cantor denoted the cardinality of the set $\mathscr{M}$ by $\bar{\bar{\mathscr{M}}}$.

This description, however appealing it might seem, does not stand logical scrutiny. It is not expressed in the language of set theory and formal logic only. The definition of cardinality as a set of all equinumerous sets was given in 1884 by G. Frege and, independently, in 1903 by B. Russell. We have already met the same idea in defining integer, or rational, numbers as sets of equivalent pairs (see page 6).

Closer analysis, however, reveals other difficulties in this definition of cardinality. For instance, this definition uses the concept of a "set of all sets having a given property." If the notion of a set is to be understood without limitations, that concept can be inconsistent. An example, due to Russell, is "the set $\mathscr{U}$ of all sets v which do not belong to themselves." This "set" $\mathscr{U}$ is not well defined. In fact, since $\mathscr{U}$ is a *set*, it is questionable whether $\mathscr{U}$ belongs to itself. But the answer "yes" to this question implies the answer: "no," and vice-versa. In fact, if $\mathscr{U}$ does belong to itself, $\mathscr{U}$ is *not* one of the v's, which implies that $\mathscr{U}$ does *not* belong to $\mathscr{U}$; i.e., to itself. Conversely, if $\mathscr{U}$ does *not* belong to $\mathscr{U}$; i.e., to itself, then $\mathscr{U}$ is one of the v's, which implies that $\mathscr{U}$ does belong to $\mathscr{U}$.

There are in set theory, various other difficulties of this and other kinds,[2] which will not be discussed here. We confine ourselves to sets of real numbers only. Real numbers have been defined axiomatically in Section 2, Chapter 1. Therefore, all sets of real numbers to be considered in this book are well defined sets, provided that we believe in consistency of the axiomatic of real numbers. However, the consistency of that axiomatic is still an open question in mathematics.

The essential importance of the concept of cardinality consists in its application to *infinite* sets. Thus, for example, the set of all natural numbers $\{1, 2, 3, 4, \ldots\}$ and the set of all squares of natural numbers $\{1, 4, 9, 16, \ldots\}$ have the same cardinality. In fact, a unique n^2 corresponds to every natural number n and vice versa.

This fact, noticed in 1638 by Galileo Galilei, was considered as paradoxical: The set of all squares is only a part (a proper subset) of the set of all natural numbers, yet both are equinumerous. This is not the only example of this kind. Analogously, the set of all natural numbers is equinumerous with its many other parts, such as the sets of all even numbers, odd numbers, cubes, prime numbers, etc. In 1888 R. Dedekind noticed that this "paradoxical" property, however, actually can be used for *defining* the concept of an infinite set: he called a set infinite if it can be equinumerous with some of its (proper) subsets.

A set is called *countable* if it is equinumeous with the set of all natural numbers. Hence, it follows that a set is countable if its elements can be arranged into an infinite sequence of elements with natural indices (and that sequence contains infinitely many different elements). Furthermore, it follows that every infinite subset of a countable set is countable.

For example, *the set of all integer numbers is countable*. In fact, every integer number A can be represented by an ordered pair, a_1-a_2, of two natural numbers A_1 and a_2 (see page 6). In order to arrange all the integers A into a sequence let us, for instance, attach to the nth integer A_n the natural index

$$n = 2^{a_1} + 2^{a_1 + a_2}$$

In this arrangement one integer may have more than one index n. For example, the integer -3 can be represented by the pairs $2 - 5$ or $4 - 7$, or by infinitely many other pairs. Thus, it would occur in the sequence infinitely many times with different indices. In order to have a one-to-one correspondence we can require that the smallest possible naturals a_1 and a_2 represent the integer A.

Analogously, *the set of all rational numbers is countable.* In fact, every rational number r can be represented by an ordered pair A_1/A_2, of two integers, A_1 and A_2 (see page 7) and, thus, eventually by an ordered set of four natural numbers, a_1, a_2, a_3, and a_4. In order to arrange all the rationals into a sequence we might take, for the nth rational, the index

$$n = 2^{a_1} + 2^{a_1+a_2} + 2^{a_1+a_2+a_3} + 2^{a_1+a_2+a_3+a_4}$$

and make a convention similar to that for integers.

Furthermore, the *set consisting of all finite sequences of natural numbers is countable.* For example, if

$$A = \{a_1, a_2, \ldots, a_k\}$$

is any such finite sequence, the set of all these A's can be arranged into an infinite sequence by taking for the nth A; e.g., the index

$$n = 2^{a_1} + 2^{a_1+a_2} + \ldots + 2^{a_1+a_2+\ldots+a_k}$$

with appropriate convention, as before.

Hence, it follows that *the set of all algebraic numbers is countable.* In fact, any algebraic number is determined by means of a finite sequence of rationals, viz. the rational coefficients of the corresponding polynomial (see page 9) and, thus, eventually by a finite sequence of naturals.

The sets of all integers, rationals, and algebraic numbers have the same cardinality as the set of all natural numbers. This gives a meaning to the statement that there are as many integers, rationals, and algebraic numbers as there are naturals.

The above facts are particular cases of a more general situation. A set consisting of elements belonging to $\mathscr{A}$ or to $\mathscr{B}$ is called a *union* $\mathscr{A} \cup \mathscr{B}$ of two sets $\mathscr{A}$ and $\mathscr{B}$. By definition

$$\mathscr{A} \cup \mathscr{B} = \mathscr{B} \cup \mathscr{A}$$

The union of more than two sets, say n sets, is defined by induction as the union of $(n - 1)$ sets and the nth set. The concept of a union can also be extended to an infinite, countable union of sets,

$$\mathscr{A}_1 \cup \mathscr{A}_2 \cup \ldots$$

We shall prove that a *finite or countable union of finite or countable sets is a countable set*. Arrange the elements of the set $\mathscr{A}_1$ into a sequence $a_{11}, a_{12}, a_{13}, \ldots$, the elements of $\mathscr{A}_2$ into a sequence $a_{21}, a_{22}, a_{23}, \ldots$, and so on. Then, the elements of the countable union $\mathscr{A}_1 \cup \mathscr{A}_2 \cup \ldots$ can be arranged into Table 2.

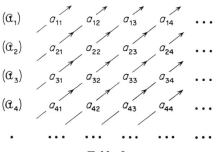

Table 2

Some of the lines in Table 2 may be finite if the corresponding set is finite. There may also be only a finite number of rows if there are finitely many sets in the union. Arrange the table into a sequence:

$$a_{11}\ a_{21}\ a_{12}\ a_{31}\ a_{22}\ a_{13}\ a_{41}\ a_{32}\ a_{23}\ a_{14} \ldots$$

as indicated by the arrows. This proves that the union is countable.

This method of proof is called the "diagonal method." Compare also page 30.

Do there exist sets which have more elements than countable sets? The *set consisting of all infinite sequences of natural numbers is not countable*. Cantor proved this by another "diagonal method." Let α be any infinite sequence of naturals, $\{a_1, a_2, a_3, \ldots \}$. Suppose that the set of all these α's is countable; i.e., it can be arranged into an infinite sequence $\{\alpha_1, \alpha_2, \alpha_3, \ldots \}$. Let

$$\alpha_1 = \{a_{11}, a_{12}, a_{13}, \ldots \}$$
$$\alpha_2 = \{a_{21}, a_{22}, a_{23}, \ldots \}$$
$$\alpha_3 = \{a_{31}, a_{32}, a_{33}, \ldots \}$$

$$\cdot \quad \cdot \quad \cdot \quad \cdot \quad \cdot \quad \cdot \quad \cdot \quad \cdot$$

To get the contradiction add 1 to each of the diagonal terms:

$$\{a_{11} + 1, \quad a_{22} + 1, \quad a_{33} + 1, \ldots \}$$

This sequence is *not* in the first line, because it differs by the first element; it is *not* in the second line, because it differs by the second element; it is in *no* line of that table, contrary to the supposition that the table contains *all* the sequences. This completes the proof.

Hence, it follows that *the set of all real numbers is not countable*. In fact, any real number can be represented by means of an infinite sequence of natural digits; i.e., by using decimal, Cantor's, or continued fraction expansion.

> To be correct, we should agree that if the expansion is finite, we consider it formally to be infinite; for example, we write 0.199 . . . instead of 0.2. Moreover, if a_{nn} is 8 or 9, we take 0 instead of $a_{nn} + 1$.

Thus, the cardinality of the set of all real numbers is not equal to the cardinality of the set of all natural numbers. The latter, however, is equal to the cardinality of all algebraic numbers. But the set of all algebraic numbers is contained in the set of all real numbers. Hence, it follows that among the real numbers there must be nonalgebraic numbers. This was Cantor's proof of the existence of transcendental numbers among reals (see page 69).

> This gives a meaning to the statement that there are less algebraic numbers than reals, and we may say that among all the real numbers there are as few algebraic numbers as naturals. How many non-algebraic—i.e., transcendental—numbers are there?

The set of *all transcendental numbers is equinumerous with the set of all real numbers*. This statement can be proved in the following way. Let $\mathscr{T}$ denote the set of all transcendental numbers and $\mathscr{A}$ the set of all algebraic numbers. Since $\mathscr{T}$ is an infinite set, it contains a countable set, say $\mathscr{P}$. Let $\mathscr{P}$ consist of all the numbers: $\pi, 2\pi, 3\pi, \ldots$. The union $\mathscr{A} \cup \mathscr{P}$ is countable. Since, the set $\mathscr{A}$ is countable, it can be arranged into a sequence with even indices. Similarly, the countable, set $\mathscr{P}$ can be arranged into a sequence with odd indices. Thus, the union $\mathscr{A} \cup \mathscr{P}$ can be arranged into a sequence with natural indices, and the two sets $\mathscr{A} \cup \mathscr{P}$ and $\mathscr{P}$, being countable, are equinumerous. Now, denote by $\mathscr{T} \setminus \mathscr{P}$ the difference between the sets $\mathscr{T}$ and $\mathscr{P}$; i.e., the set of all elements of $\mathscr{T}$ that do *not* belong to its subset $\mathscr{P}$. The set $\mathscr{T} \setminus \mathscr{P}$ is equinumerous with itself. Therefore, the set

$$(\mathscr{A} \cup \mathscr{P}) \cup (\mathscr{T} \setminus \mathscr{P})$$

is equinumerous with the set

$$\mathscr{P} \cup (\mathscr{T} \setminus \mathscr{P})$$

However, the first set,

$$(\mathscr{A} \cup \mathscr{P}) \cup (\mathscr{T} \setminus \mathscr{P})$$

is exactly the set $\mathscr{A} \cup \mathscr{T}$ of *all real* numbers, and the second set,

$$\mathscr{P} \cup (\mathscr{T} \setminus \mathscr{P})$$

is exactly the set of *all transcendental* numbers, which proves that the cardinality of the set of all transcendental numbers is equal to the cardinality of the set of all real numbers.

This gives a meaning to the statement that there are as many transcendental numbers as there are reals numbers. All the previous arguments show that cardinalities of sets, finite or infinite, can be compared. Here is an idea how it can be done generally.

Two cardinalities a and b are said to be equal ($a = b$) if they are cardinalities of some two equinumerous sets $\mathscr{A}$ and $\mathscr{B}$, respectively. We say that $a < b$ or $b > a$ if the corresponding set $\mathscr{A}$ is contained in a set $\mathscr{B}$ not equinumerous with $\mathscr{A}$. The relation of "being smaller" ($<$) between two cardinalities has properties analogous with these for ordinary numbers. For example, $a < b$ and $b < c$ implies $a < c$.

The cardinality of a finite set is considered as a natural number, indicating how many elements are in the set. Hence, it follows that the cardinality of a finite set is smaller than the cardinality of any infinite set. Cantor denoted the cardinality of a (infinite) countable set by $\aleph_0$, (aleph-zero). The cardinality of any set equinumerous with the set of all real numbers is denoted by c. By the previous definition it follows that

$\aleph_0 < c$. On the other hand, there is no infinite set of cardinality smaller than $\aleph_0$. In fact, every infinite set contained in a countable set must also be countable—thus, of cardinality $\aleph_0$.

The symbol $\aleph$ is the first letter of Hebrew alphabet. It seems likely that its shape was suggested to Cantor by the symbol ∞ (on its side) "used frequently for the designation of undetermined infinities."[3] The index "0" indicates that $\aleph_0$ is the smallest infinite cardinality. The (gothic) letter c stands for "continuum" and expresses the idea that there is continuity among the real numbers.

In set theory[4] one proves that there exist infinitely many cardinalities greater than c. Does there exist a set of cardinality greater than $\aleph_0$ but smaller than c? Conjecture denying that is called *continuum hypothesis*. There were many efforts to prove or disprove it. In 1963, P. J. Cohen[5] demonstrated that the continuum hypothesis is logically independent of the axioms one assumes in set theory; i.e., neither that hypothesis nor its negation contradicts those axioms.

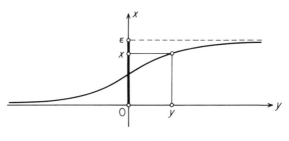

Figure 6

Thus, the cardinality of the sets of all natural numbers, integers, rationals, and algebraic numbers is $\aleph_0$, whereas the cardinality of all transcendental numbers is c, equal to the cardinality of all real numbers. Cardinality indicates, in some way, the "size" of a set. However, some sets can be "large" in the sense of cardinality but they can be "small" from some other point of view, and vice-versa.

For example, the set of all real numbers contained in any interval, however small its length, is of cardinality c. The one-to-one correspondence between all real numbers $0 < x < \varepsilon$ contained in the interval of the length $\varepsilon > 0$ and *all* real numbers y is shown in Figure 6.

Here is another example. The set of all points of the *plane* is also of cardinality c. To prove this, we first notice that a point of the plane can be represented by an ordered pair (ξ, η) of two real numbers. We wish to establish a one-to-one correspondence between all pairs (ξ, η) and all real numbers α. Take the decimal expansions of ξ and η, by assuming, as before, that these expansions are actually infinite. For example, let

$$\xi = 2.45007032000\ldots$$
and
$$\eta = 0.274062076\ldots$$

Shuffle the decimal expansion of η as given below, into the decimal expansion of ξ, to get a real number

$$2.04254000670207320006\ldots$$

which gives the required one-to-one correspondence and shows that the cardinality of all points of the plane is c. Hence, it also follows that the cardinality of all *complex* numbers is c, because every complex number can be represented by an ordered pair of real numbers. See page 10. Moreover, a segment and a square have the same cardinality c. In the same way it can be proved that sets of higher dimensions; e.g., a cube; can also have cardinality c.

Here is another example of the so-called *Cantor set*. Divide the closed interval [0, 1] into three equal parts, and remove from it the middle open interval $(\frac{1}{3}, \frac{2}{3})$. Again divide each of the two remaining closed intervals [0, $\frac{1}{3}$] and [$\frac{2}{3}$, 1] into three equal parts, and remove the middle open intervals $(\frac{1}{9}, \frac{2}{9})$ and $(\frac{7}{9}, \frac{8}{9})$. Continue this ad infinitum (which is easier to say than to realize). The set obtained as a result of this infinite operation is called Cantor set. The cardinality of this "thin" set is still c.

Proof. Expand every real number from the closed interval [0, 1] into a *ternary* expansion with the base 3; i.e., using only the digits: 0, 1, 2. See page 25. Then notice that each of the numbers that belongs to the Cantor set must *not* have the digit 1 in that ternary expansion. Within the agreement that the expansion is finite we consider it actually infinite; i.e., if the digit 2 is followed by 0's only, we replace $\ldots 200 \ldots$ by $\ldots 122 \ldots$. We first removed all the numbers between

$$\tfrac{1}{3} = 0.1000\ldots \quad \text{and} \quad \tfrac{2}{3} = 0.122\ldots$$

i.e., all the numbers in which the digit 1 immediately follows the point.

We then removed all numbers between

$$\tfrac{1}{9} = 0.0100\ldots \quad \text{and} \quad \tfrac{2}{9} = 0.0122\ldots$$

and all numbers between

$$\tfrac{7}{9} = 0.21000\ldots \quad \text{and} \quad \tfrac{8}{9} = 0.2122\ldots$$

i.e., all the numbers in which the second digit after the point is 1. We continue until at the nth step, we have removed all the numbers which have the digit 1 in their expansion, with the base 3. Therefore, the

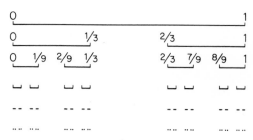

Figure 7

Cantor set consists of all numbers from the interval [0, 1], that do *not* have the digit 1 in their ternary expansion. In other words, the Cantor set consists of all those numbers which have only the two digits 0 and 2 in their ternary expansion.

Now, we substitute the symbol "*I*" for the symbol "2". Thus, the Cantor set contains all those numbers which can be represented by an infinite sequence consisting of only two symbols: 0 and *I*. But this is the expansion of any real number in the base 2. See page 26. This completes the proof that the Cantor set is equinumerous with the set of all real numbers contained in the interval [0, 1].

The Cantor set is, obviously, not dense everywhere in the interval [0, 1], because infinitely many elements are not contained in every subinterval of [0, 1] (see page 74). From the construction of Cantor set it follows that every interval contained in [0, 1], contains a subinterval *without* elements of the Cantor set. One says that the Cantor set is *nowhere dense* in the interval [0, 1]. On the other hand, the Cantor set consists of all its accumulation points; i.e., such numbers, from [0, 1], that every interval containing one of these numbers contains also infinitely many elements of the Cantor set. A set that consists of all its accumulation points is called *perfect*. Thus, to be liked, the Cantor set is perfect but nowhere dense.

These examples show that the cardinality alone gives us only partial information about how the "size" of a set. It is a natural number for finite sets, or transfinite number (e.g., $\aleph_0$ or c) for infinite sets. In a way, cardinality tells us how *many* elements there are in a set. The question "how *much*" is answered by the *measure* of a set.

2. Measure

The concept of the measure of a set generalizes such ideas as length of a line, area of a surface, volume of a body, weight of a bulk, or price of merchandise. It is a nonnegative real number indicating the size of a set, in a different way than cardinality does. In spite of the antiquity of the idea, it was only in the twentieth century that a sufficiently general concept of measure was defined. We shall discuss only the measure of sets of real numbers here. Moreover, we shall define only the meaning of the statement that a given set of real numbers is "of measure zero," without defining the concept of the measure itself.

A set of real numbers is called "of measure zero" if it can be included in a finite or countable union of intervals whose total length can be made as small as we please. We assume that the length of an interval (open or not) with the ends at α and β, $\alpha \le \beta$, is defined as $\beta - \alpha$. Other terminology is also used. One says that *almost all* real numbers, contained in a given interval (finite or not), satisfy certain condition if the remaining set of that interval (i.e., the set of numbers not satisfying that condition) is of measure zero.

From the definition above it follows that *every countable set* of real numbers *is of measure zero*. In fact, any such countable set can be arranged into a sequence of real numbers. Include the nth element of that sequence in an interval of the length $\varepsilon/2^n$, with ε positive. The total length of any union of such intervals is

$$\varepsilon\left(\frac{1}{2} + \frac{1}{2^2} + \dots\right) = \varepsilon$$

and the greatest lower bound of all positive numbers ε is zero.

Hence, it also follows that *a finite or countable union of sets of measure zero is of measure zero.* Let that union consist of sets $\mathscr{S}_1$, $\mathscr{S}_2$, ..., each of measure zero. Include the set $\mathscr{S}_1$ in a collection of intervals with the total length $\varepsilon/2$; the set $\mathscr{S}_2$ in a collection of intervals with the total length $\varepsilon/2^2$, and so on. Then the whole union of sets $\mathscr{S}_1 \cup \mathscr{S}_2 \cup \ldots$ can be included in a countable (or finite) union of intervals with the total length ε. We have exploited the fact that a countable union of countable sets is countable. See page 85.

Thus, *the sets of all naturals, integers, rationals, and algebraic numbers*, being countable, *are of measure zero.* That is, *almost all real numbers are transcendental.*

Sets that are "small" in cardinality; i.e., finite or countable, are also "small" in measure.

However, it is not true that every set of measure zero must be countable—for instance, *the Cantor set*, which is of cardinality c, (see page 89) *is of measure zero.* In fact, at its first step of construction with the interval $(\frac{1}{3}, \frac{2}{3})$ of the length $\frac{1}{3}$ removed from the interval $[0, 1]$ of the length 1, the Cantor set can be covered by two intervals, $[0, \frac{1}{3}]$ and $[\frac{2}{3}, 1]$ of total length $\frac{2}{3}$. At its second step with two more intervals, $(\frac{1}{9}, \frac{2}{9})$ and $(\frac{7}{9}, \frac{8}{9})$ removed, the Cantor set can be covered by four intervals of total length $\frac{4}{9}$. Thus, at the nth step, the Cantor set can be covered by a collection of intervals of the total length $(\frac{2}{3})^n$; the greatest lower bound of $(\frac{2}{3})^n$ for all natural n's is zero.

The Cantor set consists of all real numbers from the interval whose ternary expansion does *not* contain the digit 1. See page 90.

The above agrument, with minor modifications, can be applied to decimal expansion or to any other scale. Thus, *the set of all decimals with one or more digits missing is of measure zero.* In other words, almost all real numbers have all digits in their decimal expansions.

The frequency of occurrence of any digit is the same for almost all numbers; e.g., $\frac{1}{10}$ for decimal expansion. Moreover, the frequency of occurrence of any block of digits is the same for almost all numbers; e.g., for decimal expansion the frequency of occurrence of the block 3561 is 1/10000 for almost all numbers.

Numbers having this property with respect to some scale are called *normal* to that scale. Thus, almost all numbers are normal to any given scale. Moreover, it has been proved that almost all numbers are *absolutely normal*, which means that they are normal to every scale. However, it is not easy to exhibit an example of a normal number. The decimal

$$0.1234567891011121314\ldots$$

is normal to the scale 10. The proof is by no means trivial.[6]

It is similar with continued fraction expansions. First, notice that the set of all periodic continued fractions is of measure zero, because periodic continued fractions represent all quadratic irrationalies and, thus, all algebraic numbers of degree 2. See page 42. A fortiori the set of all Markof's numbers (see page 64) is of measure zero. Also, *the set of all continued fractions with bounded digits is of measure zero*.

Proof. We may confine ourselves to infinite continued fractions representing irrational numbers, because the set of all rational numbers is of measure zero. We also may assume that the digit $a_0 = 0$, because the set of all integers is of measure zero. Thus, let B_k be the set of all infinite continued fractions $0: a_1 a_2 \ldots$ in which all digits $a_1, a_2, \ldots$ do not exceed a fixed natural number k. Then, the set of all continued fractions with digits bounded by any natural number is a countable union of the sets $B_1, B_2, \ldots$. Since a countable union of sets of measure zero is of measure zero, it is enough to prove that each set B_k, for any natural k, is of measure zero.

To prove this, consider the set $B_k^{(n)}$ of all infinite continued fractions in which the first n digits, $a_1, a_2, \ldots, a_n$, do not exceed k, whereas the other digits, $a_{n+1}, a_{n+2}, \ldots$, may be arbitrary. Hence, it follows that the set $B_k^{(n+1)}$ is contained in the set $B_k^{(n)}$. Since the set B_k is the common part of all sets $B_k^{(n)}$ when n runs over $1, 2, 3, \ldots$, we must prove only that, for every fixed k, the set $B_k^{(n)}$ can be included in a union of intervals whose total length has the greatest lower bound zero, when n increases. To this end, we shall prove that the set $B_k^{(n)}$ can be covered by a countable union of intervals with total length

$$I_k^{(n)} \leq \left(\frac{k}{k+1}\right)^n$$

The greatest lower bound of that length is zero, when n increases, whatever the natural $k \geq 1$ is. This property of the sets $B_k^{(n)}$ will be proved by induction, with respect to n.

Let $n = 1$ and k be fixed. Consider the set $A(a_1)$ of all continued fractions $\alpha_1 = 0 : a_1 \ldots$ with given first digit a_1 and other digits, $a_2, a_3, \ldots$, arbitrary. Since

$$\frac{1}{a_1 + 1} < \alpha_1 < \frac{1}{a_1}$$

the set $A(a_1)$ is contained in an interval of length

$$I(a_1) = \frac{1}{a_1} - \frac{1}{a_1 + 1}$$

Hence, the set $B_k^{(n)}$, of all continued fractions for which $a_1 \leq k$, is the union of the sets $A(a_1)$ with a_1 running over $1, 2, \ldots, k$. Therefore $B_k^{(1)}$ is contained in the union of intervals with total length

$$I_k^{(1)} = \left(\frac{1}{1} - \frac{1}{2}\right) + \left(\frac{1}{2} - \frac{1}{3}\right) + \ldots + \left(\frac{1}{k} - \frac{1}{k+1}\right) = \frac{k}{k+1}$$

This proves the first inductive step.

Now, assume that the set $B_k^{(n)}$ can be included in a union of intervals with total length

$$I_k^{(n)} \leq \left(\frac{k}{k+1}\right)^n$$

We shall prove that for $B_k^{(n+1)}$ there is

$$I_k^{(n+1)} \leq \left(\frac{k}{k+1}\right)^{n+1}$$

This argument is more intricate. Consider the set

$$A(a_1, a_2, \ldots, a_n)$$

of all continued fractions

$$\alpha_n = 0 : a_1, a_2, \ldots a_n \ldots,$$

with the first n digits $a_1, a_2, \ldots, a_n$, fixed and others arbitrary. The set

$$A(a_1, a_2, \ldots, a_n)$$

is contained in an interval
$$I(a_1, a_2, \ldots, a_n)$$
with ends at
$$0 : a_1, a_2, \ldots, a_{n-1}(a_{n+1})$$
and
$$0 : a_1, a_2, \ldots a_{n-1}a_n$$
These finite continued fractions can be written as
$$\frac{(a_n + 1)p_{n-1} + p_{n-2}}{(a_n + 1)q_{n-1} + q_{n-2}}$$
and
$$\frac{a_n p_{n-1} + p_{n-2}}{a_n q_{n-1} + q_{n-2}}$$
respectively, where p_m/q_m is the mth convergent to α_m. See page 32. The absolute value of the difference between these ends gives length $1/(q_n + q_{n-1})q_n$ for the interval
$$I(a_1, a_2, \ldots, a_n)$$
For different $a_1, a_2, \ldots, a_n$ the intervals
$$I(a_1, a_2, \ldots, a_n)$$
are mutually disjoint, because with fixed $a_1, \ldots, a_n$ the remaining digits can be chosen arbitrarily.

Now, let $A_k(a_1, a_2, \ldots, a_n)$ be the set of all continued fractions with its first n digits fixed but with
$$\alpha_{n+1} \leq k.$$
The set A_k is contained in the set $A(a_1, a_2, \ldots, a_n)$ and is also a union of the sets
$$A(a_1, a_2, \ldots, a_n, a_{n+1})$$
with a_{n+1}, running over $1, 2, \ldots, k$. By the previous argument, each of the sets
$$A(a_1, a_2, \ldots, a_n, a_{n+1})$$
lies in an interval with ends at
$$0 : a_1, q_2, \ldots, a_n(a_{n+1} + 1)$$
and
$$0 : a_1, a_2, \ldots, a_n, a_{n+1}$$

Therefore, the set $A_k(a_1, a_2, \ldots, a_n)$ lies in an interval

$$I_k(a_1, a_2, \ldots, a_n)$$

with the ends at

$$0 : a_1 a_2 \ldots a_n(k + 1)$$

and

$$0 : a_1 a_2 \ldots a_n 1$$

These ends can be written as

$$\frac{(k + 1)p_n + p_{n-1}}{(k + 1)q_n + q_{n-1}}$$

and

$$\frac{p_n + p_{n-1}}{q_n + q_{n-1}}$$

respectively. The length of the interval $I_k(a_1, a_2, \ldots, a_n)$ is thus

$$\frac{k}{((k + 1)q_n + q_{n-1})(q_n + q_{n-1})}$$

Hence, using the same symbol for the length of an interval as for the interval itself, we have

(i) $$\frac{I_k(a_1, \ldots, a_n)}{I(a_1, \ldots, a_n)} = \frac{k}{k + 1 + (q_{n-1}/q_n)} < \frac{k}{k + 1}$$

Let $I_k^{(n)}$ be the sum of all intervals $I(a_1, \ldots, a_n)$ for which

$$a_1 \leq k, \quad a_2 \leq k, \quad \ldots, \quad a_n \leq k,$$

that is,

$$I_k^{(n)} = \Sigma\, I(a_1, \ldots, a_n).$$

Then, $I_k^{(n+1)}$ is the sum of those parts of the intervals $I(a_1, \ldots, a_n)$ included in $I_k^{(n)}$, for which

$$a_{n+1} \leq k$$

Thus, the length of $I_k^{(n+1)}$ is, at the most, the sum of all lengths

$$I_k(a_1, \ldots, a_n)$$

that is,

$$I_k^{(n+1)} \leq \Sigma\, I_k(a_1, a_2, \ldots, a_n)$$

for which

$$a_1 \leq k, \quad a_2 \leq k, \quad \ldots, \quad a_n \leq k$$

But, by (i) there is

$$I_k(a_1, \ldots, a_n) < \frac{k}{k+1} I(a_1, a_2, \ldots, a_n)$$

Hence,

$$I_k^{(n+1)} \leq \Sigma I_k(a_1, \ldots, a_n) < \frac{k}{k+1} \Sigma I(a_1, \ldots, a_n) = \frac{k}{k+1} I_k^{(n)}$$

By the inductive assumption,

$$I_k^{(n)} \leq \left(\frac{k}{k+1}\right)^n$$

Therefore,

$$I_k^{(n+1)} \leq \left(\frac{k}{k+1}\right)^{n+1}$$

To complete the proof, we must check that the set $B_k^{(n)}$ is contained in $I_k^{(n)}$ for every n, and, therefore, that $B_k^{(n+1)}$ is contained in $I_k^{(n+1)}$. In fact, $B_k^{(n)}$ is the union of all sets $A(a_1, \ldots, a_n)$, for which

$$a_1 \leq k, \quad \ldots, \quad a_n \leq k$$

and every set $A(a_1, \ldots, a_n)$ is contained in the interval $I(a_1, \ldots, a_n)$ with

$$a_1 \leq k, \quad \ldots, \quad a_n \leq k$$

However, $I_k^{(n)}$ is the union of these intervals.

This theorem may also be stated that *almost all infinite, continued fractions have unbounded digits.*

More is known about the distribution of the digits $a_1, a_2, \ldots$.[7] The natural number k occurs as a digit with the frequency

$$\frac{1}{\log 2} \log\left(1 + \frac{1}{k(k+2)}\right)$$

for almost all continued fractions. The geometric mean $\sqrt[n]{a_1 a_2 \ldots a_n}$ of the digits tends, as n increases, to a universal constant, about 2.6. The arithmetic mean

$$\frac{1}{n}(a_1 + \ldots + a_n)$$

however, tends with n to infinity. Besides, if q_n is the denominator of the convergent, $\sqrt[n]{q_n}$ tends to $\dfrac{\pi^2}{12 \ln 2}$, as n increases.

Although the set of all continued fractions with bounded digits is of measure zero, the cardinality of that set is c. Moreover, the set of all continued fractions with digits assuming only two values, say 1 and 2, is also of cardinality c. In fact, that set is equinumerous with the set of all sequences consisting of 1 and 2, which, in turn, is equinumerous with all sequences consisting of 0 and 1. The last set, however, is exactly the set of all real numbers written in binary system; i.e., with the scale 2.

Since the cardinality of all transcendental numbers is also c, it follows that there are infinitely many transcendental numbers in whose continued fraction expansions all digits are bounded, particularly if the digits assume only two values, 1 and 2.

On the other hand, the set of all algebraic numbers, being countable, is also of measure zero. It is not known whether there are algebraic numbers of degree higher than 2, in whose continued fraction expansions all digits are bounded. See also page 70.

In discussing sets "of measure zero" we have managed to this point without the concept of the measure itself. Here are some comments on that subject.

Let $\mathscr{E}$ be a set of real numbers. Include it in a finite or countable union of open intervals. Consider the total length of the intervals composing any of such coverings. The least upper bound of the total lengths for all those coverings is called the *outer measure* $\mu_e(\mathscr{E})$ of the set $\mathscr{E}$. If the set $\mathscr{E}$ is bounded (i.e., contained in some interval I with ends at $\alpha \leq \beta$) then

$$\mu_e(\mathscr{E}) \leq \beta - \alpha$$

Next, for a bounded set $\mathscr{E}$, we define its *inner measure*, as

$$\mu_i(\mathscr{E}) = (\beta - \alpha) - \mu_e(I \setminus \mathscr{E})$$

One proves that

$$\mu_i(\mathscr{E}) \leq \mu_e(\mathscr{E})$$

If

$$\mu_i(\mathscr{E}) = \mu_e(\mathscr{E})$$

the set $\mathscr{E}$ is called *measurable*, and the common value of its outer and inner measures is defined as the *measure* $\mu(\mathscr{E})$ of the set $\mathscr{E}$.

This concept of measure was introduced in 1902 by H. Lebesgue. Its importance is that it is applicable to an extremely large class of sets. The hitherto defined measures were not that general. Many, quite simple sets were not measurable by previous definitions. Strange as it might seem, the reason for those failures consisted in that one considered coverings of the set $\mathscr{E}$ by only *finite*, and not countable, unions of intervals. Allowing, in the definition, countable coverings as well proved to be crucial. For example, consider the set $\mathscr{R}$ of all rational numbers contained in the interval (0, 1). Should we admit coverings by finite unions of intervals only, the so-defined outer measure of the set $\mathscr{R}$ would be 1, whereas its inner measure would be 0. Thus the set $\mathscr{R}$ would not be measurable. However, if we use Lebesgue measure, we have

$$\mu_e(\mathscr{R}) = \mu_i(\mathscr{R}) = 0$$

and the set $\mathscr{R}$ is measurable.

The efficiency of Lebesgue measure consists in that it is *fully additive*, which means that any finite *or countable* union of measurable sets proves measurable. This was not true with the previously defined measures. Full additivity makes the class of measurable sets most extensive.[8]

Are there non-measurable sets? It was a great disappointment to Lebesgue when G. Vitali, in 1904, proved that such sets do exist. However, an assumption in set-theory, called *Axiom of Choice*, is indispensable in any proof of existence of a non-measurable set. No specific example of a non-measurable set has been exhibited by an "effective" construction; i.e., one which does not use that axiom.[9] In 1963, P. J. Cohen proved that the Axiom of Choice is logically independent of the axioms of set-theory, see page 88. This discovery again opens the question if it is consistent, with set-theory, to assume that all sets of real numbers are measurable.[10]

REFERENCES

(1) G. Cantor, *Contribution to the Founding of the Theory of Transfinite Numbers*, trans. Philip E. B. Jourdain (New York: Dover Publications, 1952), p. 86.

(2) See R. L. Wilder, *Introduction to the Foundations of Mathematics* (New York: John Wiley & Sons, Inc., 1956), Chapter 8.

(3) F. Cajori, *A History of Mathematical Notations* (LaSalle, Ill.: Open Court Publishing Co., 1930), Vol. II, par. 421, pp. 44–46.

(4) See Wilder, *op. cit.*, pp. 98–105.

(5) P. J. Cohen, *The Independence of the Axiom of Choice*, Stanford University (mimeographed), 1963, pp. 1–32.

(6) See I. Niven, *Irrational Numbers*, The Carus Monographs (New York: John Wiley & Sons, Inc., 1956), Chapter 8.

(7) See A. Khintchin, Цепные Дроби (*Continued Fractions*) (Moscow: Fizmat Isdatelstvo, 1961), pp. 92–114. There is an English translation: A. Ya. Khintchin, *Continued Fractions*, Groningen: P. Noordhoff, Ltd., 1963.

(8) The literature on this subject is very large. For one source see W. W. Rogosinski, *Volume and Integral* (New York: Interscience Publishers, Inc., 1952), Chapters 2, 3.

(9) See Wilder, *op. cit.*, pp. 71–74.

(10) See Cohen, *op. cit.*, p. 3.

Index